GAME HERITAGE

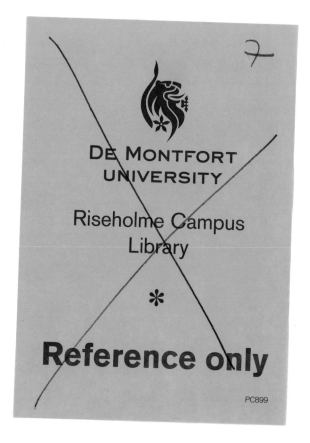

GAME HERITAGE

An Ecological Review
from Shooting and Gamekeeping Records

Stephen Tapper

The Joint Nature Conservation Committee kindly grant aided much of the analysis for this book.

The views presented are entirely those of the author.

All proceeds from the sale of this publication will go towards
research on the conservation of game and their predators.

First published 1992

Game Conservancy Ltd.,
Fordingbridge,
Hampshire.
SP6 1EF

ISBN 0-9500130-2-1

The printing costs for this publication have been supported by Eley Ltd., a subsidiary company of IMI plc.

The front cover painting, 'Snipe Shooting' was specially painted by Chris Orgill for this publication.

Printed and bound in England
by BAS Printers Limited,
Over Wallop, Hampshire

CONTENTS

FOREWORD

As a landowner lucky enough to own an upland estate in the north of England, I have always enjoyed shooting and have never seen anything paradoxical about sharing a passion for field sports with an equally strong passion for wildlife and conservation. Indeed, like many other landowners, I quickly learned that it was the income that derived from shooting that enabled me, quite simply, to manage the estate. Without that income my heather moors would have become blocks of sitka spruce or over-grazed sheep walk. It was my interest in both shooting and conservation that led to my involvement with the Nature Conservancy Council and now English Nature, as well as The Game Conservancy. There are, however, some areas of conflict. To resolve them we need not only open minds, but also clear fair-minded views of the achievements (and failings) of game management and shooting in the past. I believe Steve Tapper's account, told through the perspective of game shooting bags helps illuminate this past. I am sure it will help to reduce the misunderstandings that exist between those who shoot and those who do not.

The historical perspective is important. Man's involvement in shaping the countryside has been paramount, and as we continue to shape it in the future we must be sensitive to the needs of all sections of society concerned with rural development and conservation. We cannot afford to make many mistakes, and we need a sound understanding of the interactions between plants, animals, predators and prey before we take irrevocable decisions. The relationship between predators and their prey is a complex one and there is no doubt that in the past our forefathers saw such things in over simplistic terms. I well remember an old keeper of this era explaining to an incredulous interviewer ". . . my job was to kill everything his Lordship couldn't eat." The legacy of this attitude still haunts us today. However, in the more recent past, some conservationists have taken the equally simplistic view that predator control is really unimportant to game conservation for

shooting. For a while this was backed by the scientific establishment, even though most gamekeepers thought the notion stupid. Thanks to the scientific work of The Game Conservancy and other research organisations, we are getting closer to the truth which is that without some reduction in local abundance of the more common predators, game production is simply not enough to allow viable shooting. For me, no income from grouse shooting means no money to manage the estate. Furthermore, the habitat management made possible by this income benefits many other species of wildlife apart from game. This is acheived at no cost to the tax payer.

Population ecology is a relatively new science, and in spite of all it has taught us, one of its failings is that most studies are short-term in relation to the actual changes that may be taking place in animal numbers over many years. So I find it very rewarding that the game shooting records of estates like mine, and the daily records that many gamekeepers have kept in the past, can provide ecologists with sets of data over the long-term which they could not have obtained for themselves. Some analyses of such data, from the National Game Bag Census have appeared in the Game Conservancy's Annual Reviews in past years, and have been seen by many as unique insights into population changes. For the fox, the weasel and even the brown hare, no other long-term measures of abundance exist, and it was for this reason more than any other that the former Nature Conservancy Council (now through the Joint Nature Conservation Committee) helped to fund the work described in this book. This recognition that game management and shooting can contribute something to science is refreshing. There is much we can learn from each other whether we are landowner, conservationist, gamekeeper or scientist. This book, I believe, will help us do that.

The Earl Peel, Gunnerside. July 1992

ACKNOWLEDGEMENTS

This book has had a long incubation period and is really a joint effort. It would have been appropriate to have had a long list of those involved as joint authors on the cover, indeed at the outset that was the intention. However, the list was getting unwieldy and I was persuaded that it would help the book's identity to keep things simple. I hope those concerned will forgive me.

There are four key people whose valuable time went into this volume, and they did a lot of the hard work on which the text is based. Above all, Ayleen Clements patiently sat in front of a computer screen for eight months, deciphered my entangled *dBase* code, wrote some new programmes and eventually ran the bulk of the analyses week after week on a computer that would not win any races for speed. Mike and Gill Rands organised the collection of many historical records from old game books, and between them they handled the difficult job of tying in the old Bureau of Animal Population data with the newer National Game Bag Census information. More recently Joanne France has been invaluable in updating analyses and producing a set of graphics suitable for publication.

This book covers a wide range of species and I am lucky enough at The Game Conservancy to have many people, from scientists to sportsmen and gamekeepers, who have been able to give me a lot of advice on everything from shotgun design to details of predator/prey relationships and time-series analysis. Mike Swan has been a veritable gold mine of first hand knowledge on most aspects of shooting, and what he didn't know either Malcolm Brockless or Richard Van Oss inevitably did. On the scientific side my colleagues Nicholas Aebischer, David Baines, Nick Giles, Peter Hudson, Dick Potts, Jonathan Reynolds, Peter Robertson and Nick Sotherton have all either read parts of the manuscript or assisted with advice on content.

There are also a few who helped me at every stage, and to these people I am enormously grateful, for without their aid this book would have certainly foundered. Firstly, Don Jefferies of the Joint Nature Conservation Committee backed the project at the outset and was interminably patient with me as the time frame for completion got longer and longer. Second, the Earl Peel and his Game Conservancy Research Planning Committee gave me their full backing, but just as importantly, ensured that the money never ran out. Richard Van Oss, The Game Conservancy Director General, gave his total support, as well as some fatherly advice on cutting out some of my more outrageous assertions. Charles Nodder has been a patient editor and has masterfully steered what was a rather rough manuscript to start with through to the printers. Lastly, and most importantly Dick Potts, my boss and mentor, not only provided many insights and ideas which are peppered throughout this book, but his wild enthusiasm for the whole enterprise gave me the inspiration to see it through to completion.

Apart from the team at The Game Conservancy many others have been kind enough to allow me to use figures, drawings and data. There is no doubt that Rodger McPhail's wonderful drawings, and those of the other artists who have allowed the use of their work, have helped to bring the text and graphs in this book alive. Chris Orgill produced the eye-catching front cover. The British Trust for Ornithology allowed us to use Common Bird Census data for comparison with our own.

In conclusion, the real contributors to this book are the landowners, their agents and their gamekeepers who, for generations have kept detailed estate records in their gamebooks, and in recent years as contributors to the National Game Bag Census have allowed us to build a countrywide database from which to work. I sincerely hope that they will think their efforts have been worthwhile.

PREFACE

Man was a hunter long before he became a farmer. A million years of evolution in Africa and Europe adapted him as a pursuer of game, large and small. This evolutionary history, hundreds of times longer than the period he has been settled and civilised, has left an indelible mark on him. It is little wonder that hunting for pleasure has continued.

In Britain during historic times the right to hunt game has been vested with the landowner, unlike in North America and much of Europe where land ownership does not extend to the game on it. Thus as generations of Britons have moulded our countryside for farming and field sports, game populations have always been an important concern. Within the last two hundred years many well managed estates have kept detailed records of the game shot each year on their lands in estate game books. If the paintings of John Constable or Myles Birket Foster provide us with images of the landscape and rural life of the 19th century, perhaps the dusty ledgers of estate game books can tell us a little of the abundant game fauna during this era.

Today we look to the science of ecology to describe the patterns of animal abundance. In population ecology, methods are designed with care so that surveys and censuses are carried out without bias. However, many species have undergone long term changes in abundance, perhaps resulting from the accelerating changes to landscape and agriculture seen in recent decades. We are left with a desperate need to measure these long term variations for as many species as possible. But resources are limited and ecological surveys usually short term, also some species are more difficult to survey than others. Small territorial song-birds which advertise their presence from the tops of trees are easier to census than mammals like the weasel, which hunts quickly and quietly in thick undergrowth or in holes in the ground. So if we want to look at animal populations on a wide scale and over a long period we need a window into the past.

In this book we aim to use old shooting and game keepers' records to provide us with such a window — an old deformed pane and dirtied with time, so our picture is hazy. Nevertheless the information is well recorded and quantified. In order not to misinterpret our distorted image we must first learn something of the historical and social changes which underlie these game records. We must understand the economic basis of the estates from which they came, as well as something of the changing fashion of shooting and the technical developments of firearms and traps, all of which will have affected the numbers of game killed. Only then can we glimpse the pattern of animal abundance in a bygone era and look at changes through time.

Stephen Tapper. June 1992

AN HISTORICAL PERSPECTIVE

Evolution of the Sporting Gun

In recent centuries man's primary means of hunting game has been with firearms. These have undergone an evolution of their own with a consequent increase in efficiency. Understanding the effectiveness of the early sporting guns is essential to interpreting old shooting records.

The first practical firearms for shooting game, large fowling pieces which discharged hail-shot, were introduced in the 16th century. These worked on a match or wheel-lock principle, and since reloading was a leng-

thy process the aim was to shoot birds on the ground, killing as many as possible with a single blast. To get close to game required some careful fieldwork and one method was to use a "stalking horse"—approaching the birds on foot using a grazing horse as cover. With the exception of the punt gun used for waterfowl, this kind of shooting really has no modern equivalent.

In the late 16th century the flint-lock was introduced, and thus a standard sporting shotgun of sorts was established which remained in use for some 200 years. This

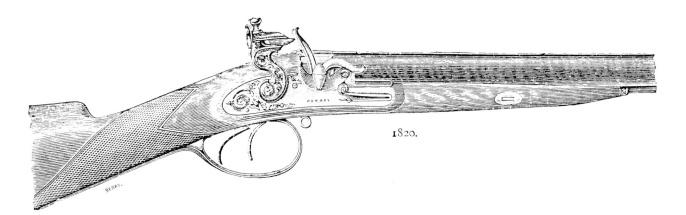

1820.

2

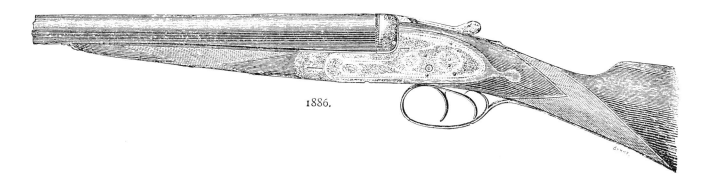

1886.

weapon had a long 40 inch iron barrel (often made from melted down horseshoe nails) and needed a wooden casing right to the muzzle. The charge was ignited by a standard flint-lock, and in operation it was very slow and somewhat hazardous. Powder was poured into the muzzle from a horn (done with some care if the barrel was already hot from a previous shot) held and rammed into place by a cork or flannel wad, on top of which a quantity of irregularly shaped shot was added. Because there was little uniformity in the quantity of either the powder or shot, and because there was a delay of at least a tenth of a second in the firing mechanism, accurate shooting of flying game birds was difficult. Most were shot on the ground or roosting in trees.

Over the years the sporting element improved somewhat, and in the early 18th century the introduction of pointing dogs made finding and shooting of game much easier. Shooting partridge while walking with dogs across autumn stubbles was considered particularly sporting. From this came the idea of shooting a flying or rising bird, further helped by two inventions. First, it was discovered that spherical shot could be made by pouring molten lead from a height through a sieve like rain drops solidifying as they fell. This gave a much better result than cutting lead sheets into little squares and shaking them around until roughly smooth. Second, a better ignition system which started the explosion from the back of the charge instead of the side considerably increased performance. Longrigg (1977) reviews this early period of sporting shooting along with other field sports of the period.

The 19th century was a period of progressive evolution in shotgun design which was instrumental in allowing

the sport of modern driven game shooting to become established. New materials such as the inclusion of steel strips with the iron, hammered together round a bar, made the first Damascus barrels in the 1820's. These were light yet strong, allowing the guns to have shorter barrels with less wooden support. This improved the balance and handiness of the gun enormously. Flint-locks were replaced by percussion caps in the 1830's, and in the 1860's muzzle loading gave way to breech loading guns which used a cartridge. Shooting became increasingly popular and London gun makers had a lucrative business inventing new weapons and refining traditional designs. Other significant advances included adding a choke to the barrel, a hammered firing mechanism and automatic cartridge ejectors—all of which came in the 1870's. Smokeless powders were introduced in the 1890's which greatly helped sportsmen to take a quick second shot instead of waiting while the smoke cleared from the first. So by 1900 the design for a standard English shotgun had been more or less perfected, and a gun produced today by London gun makers such as Purdey or Holland & Holland is almost identical in pattern to those in use ninety years ago (King, 1985).

Blanch (1909), Pollard (1923), Burrard (1932), and Crudgington & Baker (1979), all provide details of the evolution of British guns.

If the shotgun is the key to shooting, then the habitat, and particularly the farmland habitat is the key to game survival. This habitat—the rural landscape was also evolving.

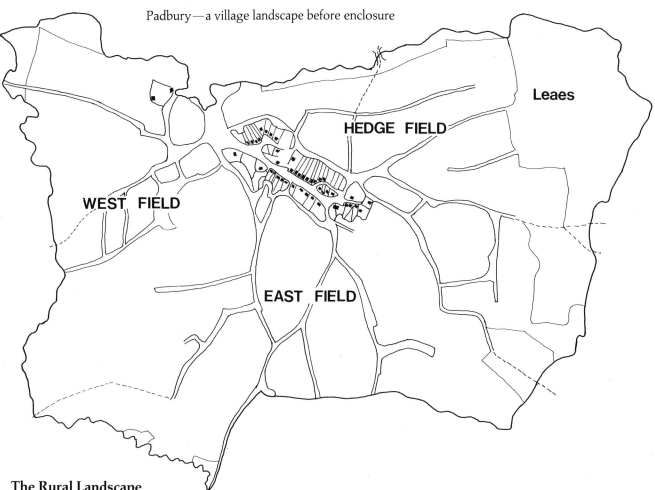

Padbury—a village landscape before enclosure

Leaes

HEDGE FIELD

WEST FIELD

EAST FIELD

The Rural Landscape

Much of rural Britain from the 16th to the 18th century was an open landscape of fen, heath and downland, used primarily as sheepwalk. Native woodlands were seriously depleted, the best timber removed for the shipping and building trades, while much of the rest was cleared for firewood and charcoal. Arable land was only one third of the total area, and the bulk of central, eastern and southern England was unenclosed and farmed under the mediaeval open field system. The basis of this was two or three large fields around each village or hamlet. These fields were subdivided into blocks or furlongs which were in turn split into separate strips allocated sequentially to different farmers in the village. In the three field system each of the main fields was rotated through cereals and fallow. A crop of wheat was autumn sown, and after harvest the field was left ploughed as a bare winter fallow. The next spring either peas, beans or barley were grown, and after this the land left a full year as fallow before the next autumn sowing of wheat.

On the chalk lands sheep were penned at night on the fallow and grazed by day on nearby open downland. The open chalkland farming systems remained largely unaltered until the late 19th century and were improved only by the development of water-meadows. These seasonally flooded pastures were created alongside many of the spring fed streams and rivers of the south.

On the clay or "cheese-lands", so called because of the emphasis on dairy produce, livestock rather than arable predominated, and the process of land enclosure was already underway at the time of the Civil War.

The enclosures set the stage for huge farming improvements during the agricultural revolution, but the process completely disrupted the mediaeval landscape pattern. Started by the landowners themselves, it was later brought about by force of Parliament, and between 1750 and 1850 there were some 2500 Enclosure Acts. Much of the land enclosed was common grazings, and in the 100 years to 1795 some two million acres (800,000 hectares) of this had been hedged in. As enclosures spread onto the cultivated land (by 1700 half of Britain's arable was enclosed) new crops and new farming systems were evolved.

A four crop rotation was developed in Norfolk in the early 18th century. The idea was that new crops of turnip and clover could be used to increase the yield of cereals. A conventional crop of winter wheat was followed by a short winter and spring fallow which allowed time to control weeds by cultivation. Turnips were sown in May and the crop hoed by hand or machine throughout the summer. The turnips were either lifted to be taken back to the stockyard for winter cattle feeding or left in the field and sheep folded on

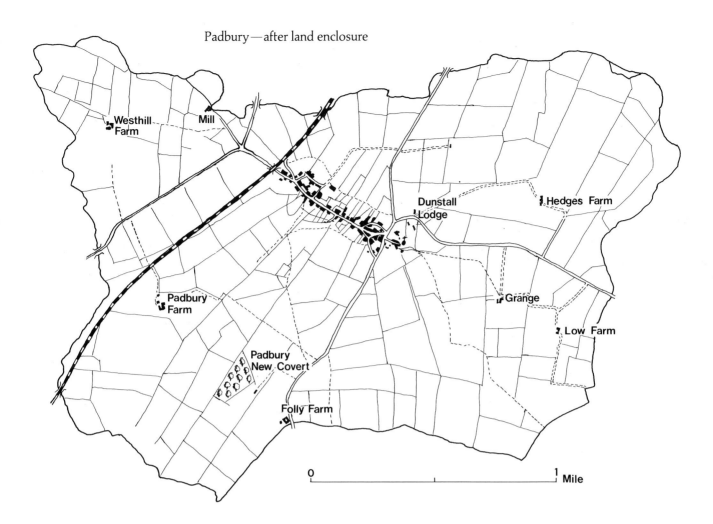

Padbury—after land enclosure

to them. In spring the field would be cultivated and put into spring barley which would be under-sown with a grass clover mix, so that after harvest a green sward would already be well established. This grass ley could be left for one or more years. The agricultural benefits of this system were profound. Increased winter fodder enabled a larger head of stock to be overwintered, which in turn increased the amount of manure produced. This enriched the soil and increased the cereal yield. A side effect of increasing livestock levels was that animal husbandry and animal breeding programmes were given a tremendous boost—the carcase weight of animals brought for slaughter doubled between 1700 and 1800.

The four-course rotation which formed the basis of the agricultural revolution remained in place throughout most of the 19th century, but towards the later half, the importance of cereal production declined in favour of a greater emphasis on livestock and dairy produce. This was the result of an increasing demand for fresh produce for the cities as well as the import of cheap cereals from the continent and the new world. To increase the grassland available to livestock, the rotation was modified so that the turnips and winter fallow were omitted and the grass ley left down for an increased number of years.

Although the 19th century saw continuous improvements in the mechanisation of farming, including the advent of steam ploughing, threshing machines and artificial phosphate fertilizers, their introduction was not always widespread and it varied considerably. The rate of their adoption depended partly on the normal cycle of boom or recession in agriculture, and partly on social factors such as the initiative of landlords in encouraging their tenants to modernise.

The country landscape, particularly the arable farmland at the end of the 19th century, was a near perfect habitat for game (Vandervell & Coles, 1980). The miles of intersecting hedges provided thick, sheltered, and well drained nesting cover for partridge and pheasant, and cereal crops formed a tall dry steppe-like habitat for foraging broods. The patchwork quilt effect produced by the rotation ensured feeding areas winter and summer for hares and game birds alike. All that was needed to release this potential was systematic management, and this depended largely on the wealth of the sporting landowners.

Harvey (1987) provides a useful summary of these farming changes and how they have affected the appearance of the British landscape, and Bettey (1970) outlines the changes in southern England.

5

The Social Framework

It was of course not just weaponry and a suitable rural habitat which created modern shooting, but the social and economic fabric as well. At the time of the first flintlock fowling pieces the shooting of game was not just a sport, it was an important means of securing fresh meat in the manorial household for the winter, since most agricultural livestock was slaughtered and salted down in the autumn.

Right from the beginning shooting has always been the prerogative of landowners, and the laws were designed to prevent anybody but the squires from having a go at the game. For example, the Game Laws of 1671 allowed game to be taken only by men with a rental income of over £100. In effect this allowed some 16,000 landowners the right to kill game but forbade the remaining 300,000 from taking any at all (Longrigg, 1977). The squires, wealthy from their rental income, were able to spend the bulk of their time on various field sports. Bettey (1970) quotes the first Lord Shaftesbury's description of the living room of a neighbouring squire who was evidently a keen sportsman and

a bit of an eccentric even then. . . .

"*. . . . strewed with marrow bones, full of hawks perches, hounds, spaniels, terriers, the upper sides of the hall hung with foxskins of this and last year's skinning, here and there a polecat intermixed, guns and keepers' and huntsmens' poles in abundance. The parlour was a large long room, as properly furnished; on a great hearth paved with brick lay some terriers and the choicest hounds and spaniels. . . .*"

As the new pattern of enclosed agriculture radically altered the appearance of the landscape and presented new opportunities for game management, it also imposed a severe strain on village life. Many small farmers with insufficient land to have a tenancy in their own right were disenfranchised and forced to become workers on the newer bigger farms. The farms themselves, which had previously been in the village, now moved out amongst their newly enclosed fields. This all tended to reinforce a rigid three tier class system of landowner, tenant farmer and labourer. Thus the gap between rich and poor widened.

At the top of the pyramid the landlords relied on rental income from their tenants. Thus it is not surprising that during the early part of the agricultural revolution they took a keen interest in farming developments and forced the pace of agricultural change. Often they would only renew leases to tenants prepared to make farm improvements. New crop rotations, improved breeds of livestock, agricultural machines and new techniques such as land drainage were all largely brought in by the landowners rather than by farmers. Some estates, like Holkham in Norfolk, became the focus of this progress. Increasing farm profits led to higher rents; at Holkham a rental income of £2,200 in 1776 was increased to £20,000 by 1816 (Longrigg, 1977). This new wealth provided the foundation for the developing interest in game management. The meticulous scientific approach that had been applied to farming was applied to game and at Holkham game records began to be kept in detail at the end of the 18th century. Bags were not large at first as the weaponry was primitive. Nevertheless "game preserves" were becoming common and professional gamekeepers more numerous.

The 18th and early 19th centuries were a time of serious division in the countryside, since much of the rural population was left landless by enclosures and later workless with the decline of cottage industries (Bettey, 1970). Unrest came in the form of riots and rick-burnings in the 1830's, but one of the commonest rural crimes was poaching. To stamp it out a series of some 33 game laws were enacted in the first half of the 19th century. Poachers and those who resisted arrest could face hanging or deportation. Such penalties did not deter the hungry labourer from town or country from trying to feed his family, they simply made him more determined. The result was that violence increased—between 1833 and 1843 a total of 42 gamekeepers were killed and many more injured. Man traps and swivel guns were employed on many estates as drastic counter measures in the poaching war. By 1823 a third of all prisoners in English gaols had been convicted under the Game Acts (Longrigg, 1977), although this may have been partly because most of the more serious criminals were either hanged or deported.

The agricultural prosperity of the 18th century was followed in the 19th by alternate periods of boom and recession. Following the Napoleonic wars agriculture went into a severe decline and many of the improvements such as drainage fell into disrepair. Farmers went broke and landowners suffered a large drop in income. Smaller landlords sold out and land became increasingly concentrated into big estates. For example in the Avon valley in Wiltshire, where there had been 50 manors in 1760 there were only 8 in 1826. By 1874 nearly a quarter of Britain comprised estates of over 10,000 acres (4,000 hectares).

In the mid 19th century, following the repeal of the Corn Laws (1846), agriculture once again boomed and arable farming was immensely profitable. This period is often referred to as the golden age of English farming. Towards the latter part of the century depression set in again as imported grain from the prairies began to arrive in quantity following the end of the American Civil War. Rental incomes went down and landowners often had a difficult job simply to fill their tenancies. Between 1875 and 1885 a million acres (400,000 hectares) of arable reverted to rough grazing; by 1900 another million had gone the same way. Over 100,000 agricultural workers were shed from the labour force during the same period (Boag & Tapper, in press). Many landowners were consequently forced to sell.

In the closing years of the 19th century many estates lost their inherited landowners and were bought up by wealthy businessmen who had made their fortunes in industry or overseas commerce (Horn, 1984). They were eager to acquire the prestige of a country house and estate. These new landowners were also keen to adopt the sporting lifestyle that went with their properties. However, because they were not dependent on the rental income of their tenant farmers they took little interest in agricultural developments and concentrated instead on improving their pheasant and partridge shoots. Shooting became a highly fashionable and competitive pastime and was given much encouragement by the Prince of Wales (Ruffer, 1989; Watson, 1978). The emphasis was on the size of the bag and anything which could increase it was adopted. There is little doubt that on many estates agriculture became a secondary consideration and the primary emphasis was on game shooting.

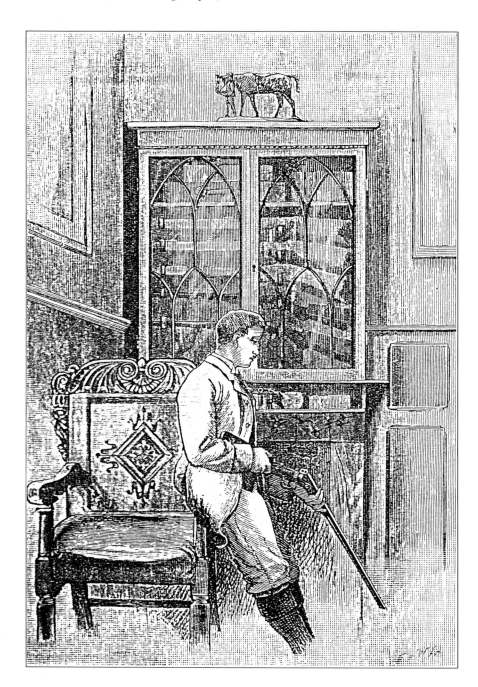

The Upland Scene

The uplands of northern Britain were once covered by dense pine forest intermixed with hardy deciduous species like birch and alder. It was the natural habitat of red deer, capercaillie, wild cat and wolf. However, after centuries of woodland clearance and grazing by sheep, the hills gradually became the colourful heather dominated landscape we now cherish. Game shooting on these upland moors has always been different in character from lowland areas where farming has had a more important influence.

In the 18th century, while game shooting with muzzle loading flintlocks was becoming an increasingly popular pastime for English country squires and other gentry, Scotland remained largely unvisited and virtually cut-off, even though game of all kinds—whether in fur, feather or fin—was available in abundance. The Scottish uplands were underexploited at this time because it required a considerable expedition to get there. The stage coach journey from London to Edinburgh lasted a gruelling ten days. However, early visitors in this era found it a sportsman's paradise, and some form of game protection was already in place by the end of the century. There were bounties on crows and birds of prey, and a proper grouse season was established by Act of Parliament in 1773.

In spite of the difficulties of access, the number of sporting tourists to the Highlands gradually increased in the early 19th century. This was encouraged by Scottish landowners who, finding their revenues from sheep in decline during this period, were able offer the well-heeled English sportsmen plenty of game relatively cheaply. To the English this upland shooting began to acquire a charm of its own. Here the sportsman still had a sense of wilderness about him, and the challenge of finding and stalking his quarry. The popularity of shooting in England had increased enormously and with intensive agriculture and game preservation, lowland shooting had to some people already developed a rather artificial air.

The crucial step in the establishment of Scotland as a sportsman's playground was the coming of rail links in the 1840's. This gave the wealthy London businessman ready access to the Highlands. The transformation must have been dramatic. No longer did he have to endure a cold and bumpy stage coach journey lasting days, with uncomfortable early starts in the morning from coaching inns. Instead he could dine at his London club, take a cab to King's Cross and board the overnight sleeper to Edinburgh. Furthermore he could take his family, his servants, and as much luggage as he needed to stay in his highland lodge for the three month season. This ease of access led directly to grouse shooting becoming a key feature in the sporting calendar. Its popularity with Queen Victoria and Prince Albert at their retreat at Balmoral, which they had purchased in 1852, made it even more fashionable.

By the end of the 19th century grouse shooting was so popular that demand often outstripped availability. Most grouse shooting was to be had on a rental or long-term lease basis. This pressure led directly to more intensive shooting and the kind of competitive spirit towards achieving large bags that was becoming common in the lowlands. Heather burning, which had been started to improve sheep grazing, was also adopted to achieve a better and more consistent habitat for grouse. To shoot the number of birds that was seen as socially desirable, walking up grouse was gradually abandoned on the more productive moors in favour of driving over a line of permanently constructed grouse butts. It also enabled the older, stouter, and less fit members of the party the opportunity to show off their shooting skills. This pattern of shooting became the norm and has been the tradition of grouse shooting ever since. It has remained intact throughout the 20th century and the open moorland areas have not been subject to the intense agricultural pressures of the lowlands, even though there has been an erosion of moorland through the encroachment of forestry and overgrazing by sheep.

Eden (1979) provides an vivid account of the development of shooting in Scotland.

THE LAST 100 YEARS

The early part of this century marked the high point of game shooting. Not only was game more abundant than it had ever been but it was a major force in moulding the British landscape and scenery. In the uplands the heather moors were kept open and regularly burnt, with a patchwork mosaic providing optimum conditions for grouse and other open-ground nesting birds. Everywhere in the lowlands broad-leaved and mixed woodlands were planted, retained and managed for pheasants. On farmland, hedgerows were tended and conserved as partridge nesting habitat.

During the first half of this century, however, there was a decline in formal driven game shooting based on large numbers of wild birds. This came partly from the intensification of agriculture squeezing out habitats for wildlife, and partly from shifts in society with fewer landowners wealthy enough to afford the lifestyle of their parents. These changes were inevitable with advancing social attitudes, but they were accelerated by the two world wars.

The First War closed the curtain on the polarised class structure of the Victorian and Edwardian eras, together with the sporting life that much of the gentry enjoyed. The continuity of game preservation by land owners and their gamekeepers was cut down in the muddy battle fields of northern Europe. Although strenuous efforts were made to recover after 1918, and on the larger estates game management was restored to an efficient but somewhat lower level, the Second War swept away the last of the integrated fabric of game management which had formerly knitted together the rural landscape. In 1946 virtually all game shooting had ceased.

Since the war, with the break up of many estates and with financial and agricultural pressures, game conservation and shooting has taken on a different complexion. The managed land is fragmented, with units often separated by large tracts devoid of a gamekeeper. Wild game management is no longer widespread, although shooting remains a very popular sport. Indeed it is arguable that it is as popular today as it has ever been, with probably about 542,000 people participating (Cobham Resource Consultants, 1992) including rough shooters, farmers, syndicate guns, gamekeepers and landowners.

Changes in the Landscape

The character of upland grouse moors has changed very little in comparison with lowland game habitats. However, the extent of the moorland has declined considerably. Some of this erosion has been intentional such as the loss to forestry and to farming, but much has been unintentional through the invasion of bracken or overgrazing by sheep. This latter process continues today; for heather is disappearing from many upland areas because agricultural subsidies are leading to high stocking rates of sheep. This leads to a gradual fragmentation of grouse habitat which makes management more difficult.

In the lowlands, changes in agriculture have transformed much of the landscape. The general trend over the last hundred years has been one of long periods of depression followed by rapid expansions in production. Recession and boom are most clearly reflected in the amount of arable land and the area under cultivation (tillage)—Fig 1.1. For the most part these two total acreages have paralleled each other and they document

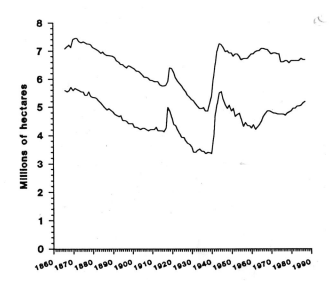

Fig 1.1 Changes in the amount of arable land (crops & temporary grass)—top line, and tillage (annual crops)—bottom line, in Great Britain. Based on Ministry of Agriculture June returns.

the gradual decline in British agriculture up to the outbreak of the Second World War, with only a minor recovery during the First. The decline in farm profitability was largely the result of cheaper produce from overseas—in particular wheat from the American prairies. To some extent game preservation benefited from this decline, because many landlords who relied on income from tenant farmers were forced to sell to the affluent *nouveau riche* who wanted country estates for sport and were able to devote much of their wealth to this end. Only after the predicament produced by the Atlantic U-boats in 1941 was the strategic importance of arable farming realised and since then it has received a high level government support.

Although the amount of arable land is now more or less equivalent to what it was a century ago, qualitatively it is very different. Farming systems are now highly specialised, whereas in late Victorian times most farms were mixed arable and livestock enterprises. The change arose in the 1920's and 1930's when many small west country farms gave up their unprofitable arable crops and then, as things recovered after the war, went into intensive dairy or livestock production. In eastern England by contrast, new post war technologies allowed them to concentrate on profitable crops and dispense with livestock altogether. This trend is evident from the maps in Fig 1.2. A major contributing factor was the introduction of artificial fertilizers, enabling arable farmers to dispense with the traditional rotations which had been used to build up soil fertility. Clover leys, livestock and farm manure were replaced by bags of nitrogen and a continuous succession of arable crops—mostly cereals.

Accompanying specialization was a process of modernisation. Tractors and combine harvesters not only reduced the manpower needed to run an arable operation, but because the machines worked more quickly, they also led to increased field sizes. This process has been most marked recently, and for conservationists a lamentable farming trend. For example Pollard, Hooper & Moore (1974) estimated that half a million miles (800,000 km) of hedge were lost in England and Wales during the post war decades. Almost equally distressing has been the widespread and burgeoning use of farm sprays which have had a dramatic effect on the flora and fauna of cereal fields. The effects on wildlife have been profound and many are only just coming to light after years of research. The impact of some was sudden, such as the severe reduction of species like the peregrine falcon and sparrowhawk through the use of organochlorine seed dressings, like dieldrin, which built up in the food chain eventually killing these top predators. Less obvious, and to some extent undetermined, has been the way herbicides have reduced the floral diversity of farmland, which in turn has depleted insect numbers and the species which depend on them—including the grey partridge.

Changes in Shooting

In late Victorian Britain, game shooting was reaching a pinnacle of development and was the height of sporting fashion, spurred on by a flamboyant Prince of Wales as one of its keenest protagonists. Not only was shooting fashionable, but prowess on the shooting field was considered an essential gentlemanly accomplishment.

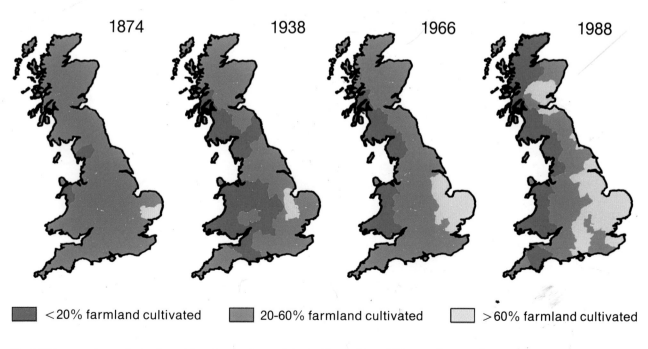

Fig 1.2 The growing polarisation of farming systems. Adapted from : Boag & Tapper (in press).

This engendered a highly competitive spirit and the size of an individual's bag at the end of the day could be source of pride or embarrassment. The scale of these bags would doubtless cause outrage if they were achieved today. For example, the Maharajah Duleep Singh shot 780 partridge in a single day at Elveden in Suffolk (Turner, 1954) and the most astonishing of all was Lord Walsingham who killed 1070 grouse in a day at Blubberhouses in Yorkshire (Ruffer, 1989).

To reach these levels estates had to be laid out to hold maximum numbers of birds, with drives organised so that a continuous supply of game could be made to fly over the guns, presenting a constant stream of diverse and challenging targets. The flying qualities of the birds, their behaviour and their habitat meant different strategies for each of the main quarry species, pheasant, partridge and grouse. The methods of driving that evolved in the late 19th and early 20th century have remained virtually unchanged to the present day.

For pheasants, large and straight flying game birds, the greatest challenges are presented by birds that fly high. To present birds in this way is not easy, as pheasants are pretty reluctant to fly at all, and getting them off the ground instead of skulking around the floor of the wood can be a real problem. Gray (1986) gives many examples of how this is achieved in all sorts of lowland situations. The best way is to have carefully planned coverts between 200 to 500 metres apart so birds driven out of one will fly to another (Fig 1.3). This

allows guns to be placed in a position between to take the birds in full flight and at maximum height and speed. Two strategies are adopted to get the birds high enough; in hilly country, woods on tops of the hills and guns in the valley bottoms is a simple solution. Alternatively, or in addition, birds can be made to fly out over tall trees through special gaps in the canopy. Flushing points are made for this purpose (Fig 1.4).

For grey partridges the skill is shooting birds that fly fast, can twist and turn, and often come over in coveys that break up unpredictably when above the guns. Partridges don't fly very high but it is still quite important to get the birds up a bit before they are shot at. This is often achieved by allowing some hedges to grow tall or planting shelter belts, and driving birds over these to increase their height. Partridges, being farmland birds, need to be driven off open ground, not out of woods. A lot beaters are required (often 20 to 30), and an area from 50 to 100 hectares (125 to 250 acres) is typically surrounded to enclose enough birds (Potts, 1986). On open ground partridges tend to flush fairly early and on fields of new sown crops or short stubble driving can be quite difficult. The best strategy is to locate the guns near a field of roots or other tall crops so that birds can be swept into this field first; then during the final beat through the roots the birds will flush close to the beaters and be more easily steered over the guns (Fig 1.5). This method enables birds to be presented in small numbers rather than in a massive flock (Stanford, 1963).

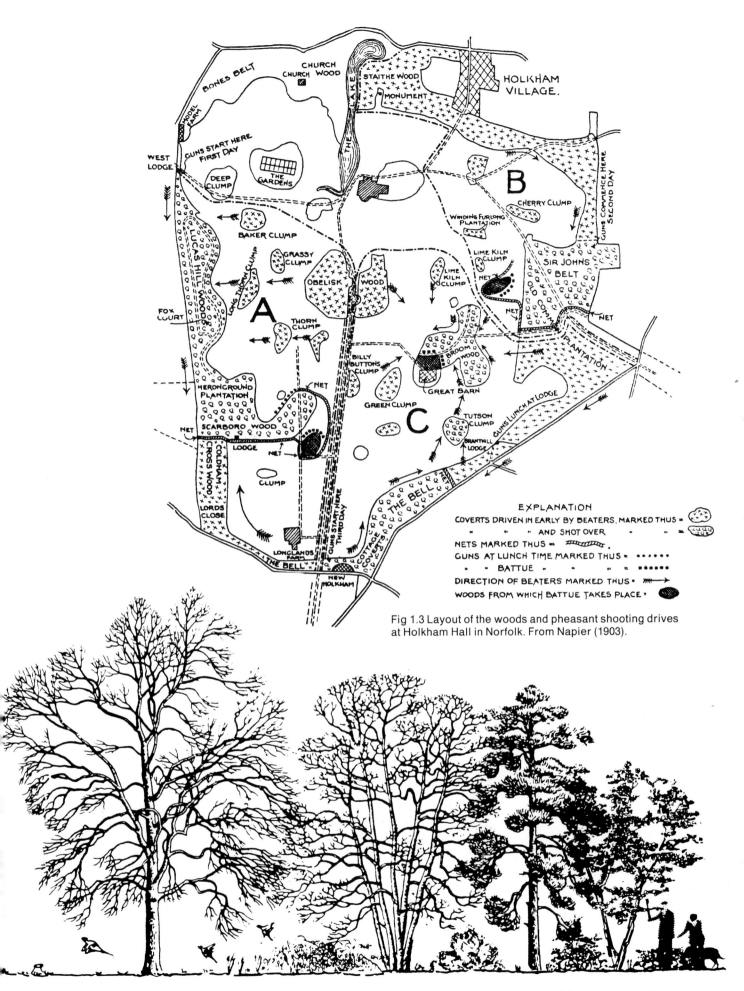

Fig 1.3 Layout of the woods and pheasant shooting drives at Holkham Hall in Norfolk. From Napier (1903).

EXPLANATION
COVERTS DRIVEN IN EARLY BY BEATERS. MARKED THUS =
"   "   "   "   AND SHOT OVER   -   "   " =
NETS MARKED THUS =
GUNS AT LUNCH TIME MARKED THUS = ••••••
-    " BATTUE -   "   " = ••••••
DIRECTION OF BEATERS MARKED THUS •
WOODS FROM WHICH BATTUE TAKES PLACE •

Fig 1.4 Section of a pheasant covert showing how breaks and different tree heights can be used to drive pheasants out of a wood and increase their height. From Gray (1986).

Grouse shooting follows a similar strategy. However, topography is important as grouse often tend to follow the contours of the hill rather than fly up or down. Lack of natural cover means that special butts need to be created to conceal the guns. Grouse tend to fly higher than partridges and tend to group together into packs, so that large numbers can fly over the guns at any one time (Fig 1.6). A typical day for 8 guns might consist of 4 or 5 drives of 80 to 240 hectares (200 to 600 acres) using perhaps 16 beaters (Hudson, 1986a).

These principles of driven shooting are as relevant today as they were 90 years ago. Woods are still managed and planted for pheasants, moorland and farmland is still adapted to accomodate grouse and partridges. However, the shooting clientele has changed considerably. Most landowners can no longer afford to retain all the shooting for themselves, their family and friends. To run a viable enterprise on an estate these days may mean leasing whole beats to a syndicate or letting shooting by the day to paying guests. While this has had the beneficial effect of retaining the game management and providing income, which can offset the loss in farm earnings which taking land out of production for spinneys or game crops inevitably has, it has led to an increase in "commercialism". This has not been welcomed by all. Commercialism leads to pressure for an increased number of shooting days, often with paying clients who are relatively naïve to country traditions and may be seduced into believing that the size of the bag is more important than the quality of the shooting. To acheive large bags gamekeepers have come to rely much more on hand rearing gamebirds, rather than encouraging the wild ones as they have traditionally done in the past.

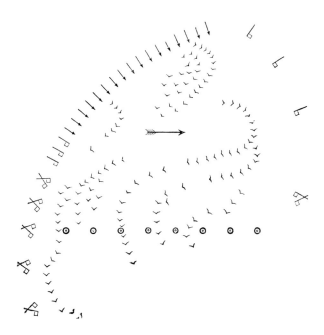

Fig 1.6. Final stages of a difficult red grouse drive with a strong cross wind (shown by large arrow). The line of gun butts is shown by circles, beaters by arrows, and the flags indicate the position of flankers and stops. The direction the birds usually take is show by the chevrons. From Payne-Gallwey (1902).

Changes in Gamekeeping

The key ingredient in producing wild gamebirds in all habitats has always been predator control. It is a strategy which has often been perceived by the general public as persecution, and by some ecologists as unimportant to game population dynamics. In recent years, however, its significance is becoming more appreciated (see Reynolds, Angelstam & Redpath, 1988).

A wide range of predators will take either adult gamebirds, chicks or their eggs. Old time gamekeepers referred to anything from a rat to a badger, or a jay to an eagle as vermin. However, the fox, stoat, carrion crow and magpie are now regarded as the most important, since their predation is both systematic and concentrated, particularly during the gamebird nesting period.

Trapping, shooting, and in the past, poisoning have been the main methods of the gamekeeper. Over the years he has adapted his ways as new trap designs and approaches to predator control have become available. However, change has mainly been forced on him as increasingly protective legislation has outlawed his techniques and protected more species.

When much of Britain was keepered, over 80 years ago, and when labour was cheap, the main strategy in areas like north west Norfolk was to eliminate most of the carnivorous birds and mammals. Thus traps and baits

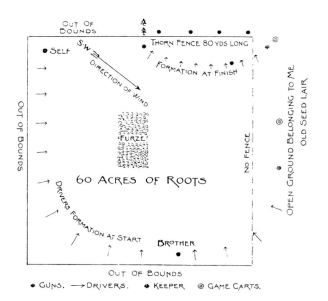

Fig 1.5 A partridge drive from a field of roots. From Fryer (1903).

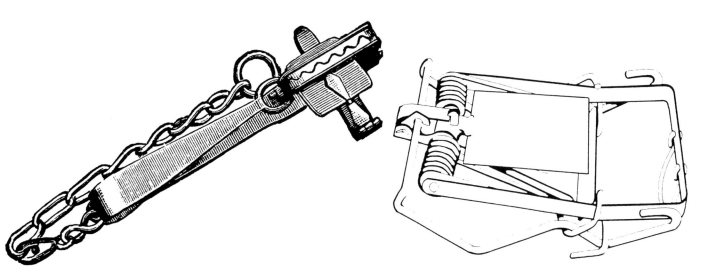

Fig 1.7. A small Dorset gin trap designed for small ground vermin (now illegal).

Fig 1.8. A modern Fenn trap for use in tunnels so that the jaws kill the animal outright across the back or neck.

were set all year round to prevent invasion from outside. Today's keeper knows this is not usually necessary, so his effort is condensed into the period when his game is most vulnerable; the spring for wild game and autumn for hand-reared birds. He is likely to focus only on those few predators he knows to be a problem.

Poisoning was the first method to be outlawed as a means of predator control (Protection of Animals Act 1911), but the practice has continued to be used illegally for killing corvids and foxes. The reason for this misuse is partly because it is easy to lay poison baits without

being caught, and partly because other legal methods are much less effective. The actual poisons used have varied with their availability for other legal purposes. For example, for many years, a keeper could get hold of strychnine to poison moles, and alphachloralose could be obtained for use against pigeons, rats and mice. Neither of these chemicals is now obtainable by the public, except under licence.

The basic trap used by keepers over generations since the start of game preservation was the gin (Fig 1.7). This was a highly adaptable device which could be just

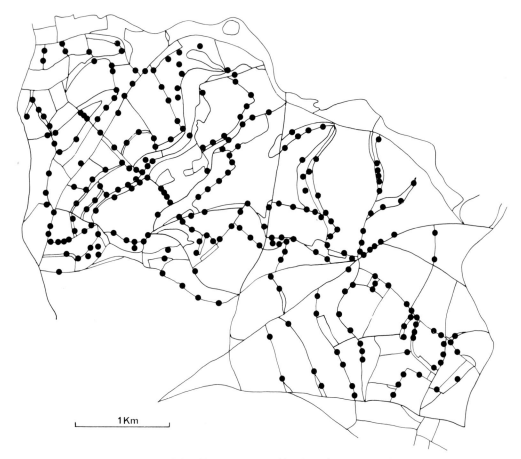

1Km

Fig 1.9. A network of tunnel trap sites containing Fenns operated by three keepers each spring on a Sussex downland shoot.

as easily put in a hole to catch a stoat as set in the open for a fox. Other traps were used for special jobs, such as egg traps for crows, and pole traps for buzzards, harriers and other raptors. The biggest single use for the gin was as a means for killing ground vermin; weasels, stoats, hedgehogs and rats, and for this the keeper employed a large number around all the hedges and woods on his beat.

In 1954 the Pests Act made it mandatory to use only Ministry of Agriculture approved traps and in 1958 approval for the gin was removed. The most successful replacement for the gin was the Fenn trap (Fig 1.8), designed to kill ground vermin more humanely. Use of these traps was precisely defined in the legislation, in particular they had to be set in tunnels—never in the open. Many keepers now use a network of these tunnel traps to reduce ground predator numbers to a spring minimum (Fig 1.9). A hundred traps per keeper per 400 hectares (1000 acres) is considered sufficient.

The outlawing of the gin trap made the job of fox control more difficult, and this has probably contributed to increasing fox abundance. Initially keepers switched to a combination of wire snares and gassing at the earths. The gassing technique, a simpler and less time consuming operation than digging out and using terriers, evolved from the use of hydrogen cyanide gas for rabbit control. It was permitted for use against foxes as a result of the Agriculture Act (1947), but it is now illegal due to the provisions of the Food and Environment Protection Act (1985). Self locking snares were banned in the Wildlife and Countryside Act (1981). Since the 1970's many keepers have come increasingly to rely on night shooting with a rifle and a high intensity spotlight.

In the early part of this century the gamekeeper looking after partridges or grouse really only had two duties, catching poachers and destroying vermin. To the latter he was able to devote most of his time so it was carried out with uncompromising severity and any animal or bird which took the occasional game chick was eliminated. Most of Britain was covered with a contiguous network of well keepered estates, so that virtually every corner of the countryside was subject to this continuous destruction of vermin on a scale that is almost unbelievable today. The extent of this can be worked out from the number of gamekeepers in each county, enumerated in the 10 yearly National Censuses for England, Wales and Scotland.

Between 1871 and 1911 the numbers of gamekeepers was increasing, reaching a peak of 23,056, but subsequent censuses showed huge reductions to 1951 when only 4,391 were recorded (Fig 1.10). Determining the present day number in Fig 1.10 has been rather more difficult and subject to error. Because of dwindling numbers, the census office has lumped gamekeeping along with other trades such as gardeners and domestic servants when doing the analysis of the most recent surveys. Nevertheless the individual returns still retain the term gamekeeper as a profession. In the 1981 census there was a more detailed breakdown of trades based on a sub-sample which separated the gamekeeper category. Extrapolation from this sample suggests a present day figure of 1,790 for England and Wales and another 720 for Scotland—about 2500 in total*.

*[Statistically the errors on these last totals are quite high; for example, the England and Wales figure of 1,790 is actually based on 9 occurrences in a 0.5% sample (115,021 people). This would give an upper 95% confidence limit of 2,989 and a lower one of 590 to the England and Wales estimate].

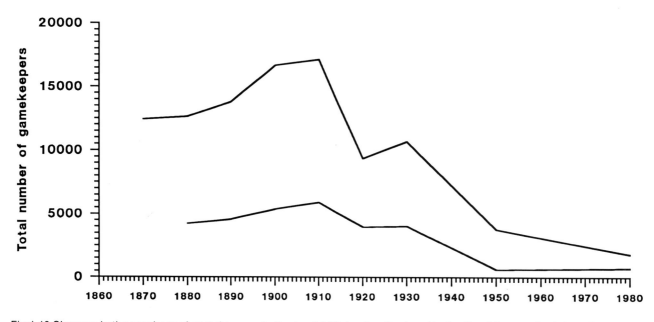

Fig 1.10 Changes in the numbers of gamekeepers in England & Wales (top line) and in Scotland (bottom line). Data from the National Censuses to 1951 and 1981 figures calculated from a sub-sample—see text.

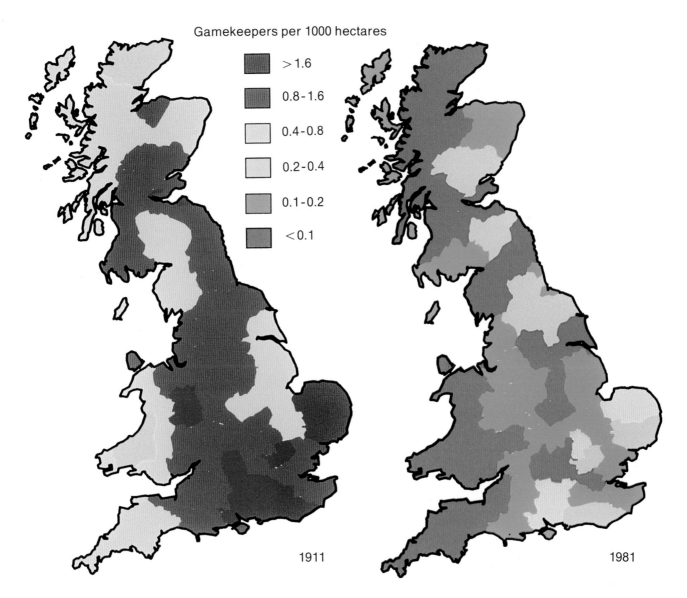

Gamekeepers per 1000 hectares

■	> 1.6
■	0.8 - 1.6
□	0.4 - 0.8
□	0.2 - 0.4
■	0.1 - 0.2
■	< 0.1

1911

1981

Fig 1.11. Gamekeeper numbers per 1000 hectares in each county in 1911 and 1981. Data from the 1911 National Census and calculated from a subsample in 1981—see text.

In order to translate this into an assessment of the change in level of predator control we have to take account of one other factor. In recent years, because of the high cost of employing a full-time keeper, many landowners or shooting tenants have employed part-time or amateur keepers, and many small farmers and shepherds do gamekeeping work as well. Clearly these individuals would not appear in the National Census. However, in The Game Conservancy's own National Game Bag Census we ask contributors to specify such part-timers as "half keepers". In our sample these part-timers represent an additional 20%. So for the comparative maps in Fig 1.11 we have assumed a total keeper population of 3000 for 1981. The 1911 census lists the total number of keepers within each county, but for 1981 we have had to estimate these based on the distribution of keepers in the National Game Bag Census. Comparison of the two maps shows that nowhere today do gamekeepers come anywhere near to the number that were present in Edwardian times. One

gamekeeper can effectively manage 400 hectares (1000 acres) of ground, so a well keepered estate would have 2.5 keepers for every 1000 hectares (2500 acres). In 1911 in Norfolk there were 2.25 keepers per 1000 hectares—clearly the whole county was keepered.

The effect of this scale of predator control on birds of prey and carnivores was devastating. Moore (1956), Brown (1976), Watson (1977) and Langley & Yalden (1977) have shown that the distributions of buzzard, red kite, hen harrier, pine marten, polecat and wildcat were all reduced in the early 19th century to those small parts of Britain where keepers were least numerous. (Fig 1.12). The fact that these animals have been recovering as gamekeeping continues to decline lends strong support to the argument that it was indiscriminate predator control which caused their near extinction a hundred years ago. It is ironic that today professional gamekeepers appear closer to extinction than some of the animals they once persecuted.

17

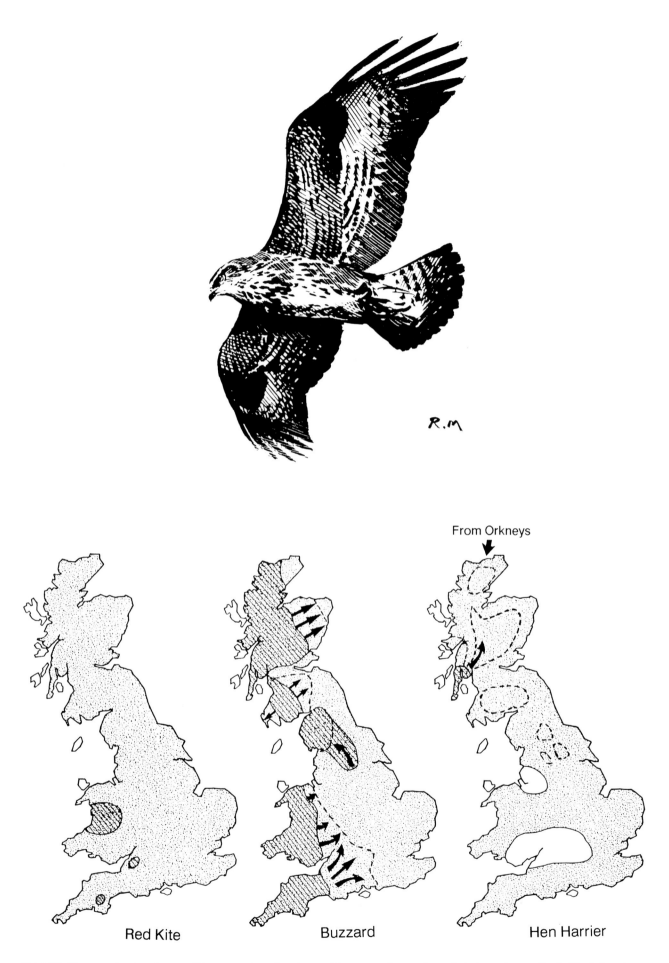

Fig 1.12. Changes in abundance of three species of raptor and three carnivores thought to have been affected by intensive game preservation early this century. Stipple shows former 18th century range, cross hatch the minimum range in the early 20th century, and arrows and broken line the range extensions since then.

18

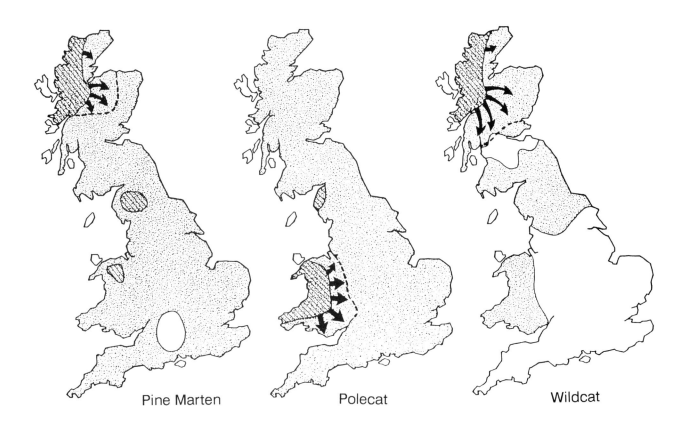

Pine Marten   Polecat   Wildcat

INTRODUCTION TO THE
SPECIES ACCOUNTS

One aspect of estate management in which shooting has played an integral part is a tradition of accurate record keeping. Details of the game shot have been recorded in ledgers or game books, sometimes for more than a century. These game books, usually laid out with a column for each species, recorded the activities on each shooting day; the various guests that were present, what drives took place and of course the exact numbers of game that were killed. Often owners added informative comments and remarks about the day as well. At the end of the season the bag of each species was totalled so that there was a summary line for each year.

Not only were these game books a diary and history of the shooting, they were also used by the owner as a record of the success of game management on his estate. Indeed they were a permanent record of the sporting value of an estate. Records from individual estates reflect individual and local acheivements, but if data from a large sample of game books can be combined, they provide an insight into changing game abundance. It was this idea of using a recording system that was already in place, and formalising it into an annual national survey, that led to the setting up of the National Game Bag Census in 1961. The National Game Bag Census has provided The Game Conservancy with the raw information that we have analysed species by species in this book. For a more detailed explanation of the history and origins of the census, together with a discussion of some of the more complicated methods of analysis, the reader should consult the Appendices starting on page 112.

In the chapters that follow, we are mainly interested in a comparison between species, so we have chosen to perform a broadly similar analysis for all species. We then present additional analyses appropriate to each to illustrate key aspects of the data.

Two analyses which are common to all are the national game bag trend since 1961, and the geographical distribution of this bag based on county boundaries. For those game species which are well recorded in pre-war game books we have also calculated a long-term trend since 1900 and a pre-war geographical distribution.

The Sample Unit—Bag Density

The basis for most of our analysis is the number of animals killed per square kilometre (abbreviated to km², which is 100 hectares or 247 acres), per year, per estate. This is the bag density. To calculate this, the key facts required for each estate for each year are, the area of the shoot and the total number of game shot by species. Bag records without the estate area cannot be used, neither can personal shooting records kept by individuals who shot in a variety of places. Using bag density as the sample unit gives equal weight to all estates irrespective of their size.

This then is the basic unit of comparison between areas and years: the number killed per 100 hectares on each shoot in one year. These units are then grouped by county, by region, or by year to calculate trends and distributions.

National Trends

The national trends shown in this book are annual averages, calculated as untransformed means with two standard errors to approximate 95% confidence limits.

These confidence limits, indicated on the graphs by an error bar above and below the calculated average point for each year, indicate the probable error around each point. Statistically, this means that if we were to obtain another different sample of estates from the same year we could be certain, with a 95% probability, that this new average would fall within the region enclosed by the bars. The national trend figures given for each species since 1961 are calculated in this way and based on an average of all estates—not an average between regions. When comparing years, the significance of variations can be assessed with these confidence limits. Where error bars do not overlap, significant differences are present. Where error bars are not shown it is because sample sizes are too small to show statisically significant differences.

Long-term Trends

The long-term trends computed for some species are in the main calculated in exactly the same way as the national trends for the 1961-85 period, except that error bars are not shown. These long-term trends are based on including only those estates that have virtually continuous data since the turn of the century (90% of years returned). Because we use these long-term trends to illustrate particular points we have often separated this group into upland or lowland estates, or regionally.

Geographical Distributions

To show the regional variation between counties we have used the same sampling unit (bag density) and calculated a county average for all the estates and available years within the county. Thus, if for the period 1961-1985, five estates submitted 10 years worth of data within a county, then we have a sample of 50 bag density estimates from which to calculate the average. We have not calculated confidence limits on these estimates or tried to assess the significance of differences between counties since our sample units are clearly not independent.

The pre-war geographical distribution of the bag covers a slightly longer time frame (38 years) compared to the post war (25 years). We considered this appropriate since the pre-war data covers fewer estates and it allowed us to use virtually all the available data.

Population cycles

Populations of some species fluctuate up and down in a cyclic fashion, and in species like red grouse and mountain hare this is quite marked. Game bag records often provide sufficient data to allow this phenomenon to be examined in detail in a statistical way. This kind of statistical analysis (known and time series analysis) shows what the average length of the cycle is and how strong it is in relation to what might be considered the random effects of weather or other enviromental pressures which affect game populations annually. Details are explained in Appendix II (page 118).

In Summary

The quality of information we get from game bags for the different species of game or predator varies enormously with the way they are recorded by the contributing estates. For the key game birds like, grouse and woodcock, the details registered in game books are almost always a very accurate record of precisely what was taken on the estate during each season. For other animals, such as rabbits and woodpigeons, records from game books usually only provide partial information, since individuals killed through pest control operations may well be left unrecorded. Different methods of analysis are often appropriate to different species. It is important therefore to understand the framework within which records for each species have been collected and part of the purpose of the narrative accompanying each of the following species accounts is to provide the reader with this insight as well as information on how each animal has fared in a game management context.

THE GAME

Rabbit *(Oryctolagus cuniculus)*

The rabbit is not a native of the British Isles, but was brought here by the Normans in the 11th or 12th century. Even then they were not really wild animals, and most were kept in enclosed rabbit warrens designed to be a ready source of fresh meat for the nobleman's kitchen. With time these warrens gradually developed into large scale commercial enterprises, and by the late 18th century a whole industry was producing rabbit meat and fur—the latter primarily for felt hats. Concurrent with this, forest clearance and a steady reduction in the numbers of native predators was helping to produce a more conducive environment for those rabbits that escaped.

The commercial rabbit warren reached its maximum importance around 1800, after which time its economic significance diminished (Sheail, 1971). This decline in rabbit keeping resulted from twin economic pressures. First, more efficient farming meant that land could be more profitably used for cereal growing or for conventional livestock. Second, the rabbit market was being gradually taken over by cheap imported products from Australia and New Zealand, where, after their introduction in the early 18th century, rabbits had quickly overrun large tracts of country in the absence of any serious native predators (see Thompson & Worden, 1956). As the British enclosed populations were abandoned, many deteriorated into open unmanaged wild warrens, and some of these were used for sporting shooting. However, some commercial warrens, for example the Lakenheath warren near Elveden were still kept going until the end of the 19th century (Turner, 1954).

With the decline of the enclosed warren and a burgeoning wild rabbit population, increasing emphasis was placed on control to reduce agricultural damage. Thus the art and techniques of the warrener were passed to the rabbit catcher, who operated throughout the estate reducing numbers as much as possible. His methods were ferreting, trapping and long netting—shooting was not an important technique. Much of the warrener's

time had also been spent in maintaining the earth banks which surrounded the warren. Feeding supplementary food to the rabbits in winter was also important, as well as getting rid of any stoats, rats, hedgehogs, and other predators that had taken up residence inside the boundaries (Turner, 1954).

As increasing emphasis was placed on agriculture, areas of down, breckland, and former rabbit warren, were ploughed up, and rabbits were kept out with the newly invented wire netting. Another invention of significance was the gin trap. The Ground Game Act of 1880 gave tenant farmers the right to control rabbits and hares to protect crops, and the gin trap gave them a quick and effective tool. An unforeseen consequence of this Act was that it actually encouraged farmers to exploit wild rabbits, and their practice of using hundreds of gins set in the open also accounted for many predators. It has been argued that the Ground Game Act in this way helped to increase rather than decrease rabbit numbers (Lockley, 1964).

During the Second World War the offensive against rabbits was renewed, and bag records before the myxomatosis epidemic of 1953/4 suggest that numbers were already in sharp decline (Fig 2.3). However, after the myxomatosis epizootic had killed over 99% of all British rabbits, the whole system of rabbit control had to be altered. The policy shifted from one of control to one of clearance—to this end Rabbit Clearance Societies were formed and they received a government subsidy in the form of cartridges until 1971. Myxomatosis also swept aside what was left of the rabbit industry, as few people were prepared to buy meat which might have come from a diseased animal. This emphasis on getting rid of rabbits at any cost also heralded new methods of control such as gassing. The loss of rabbits was a considerable benefit to farmers and large areas of downland which hitherto had been useless for agriculture because of the rabbits were ploughed and brought into cultivation.

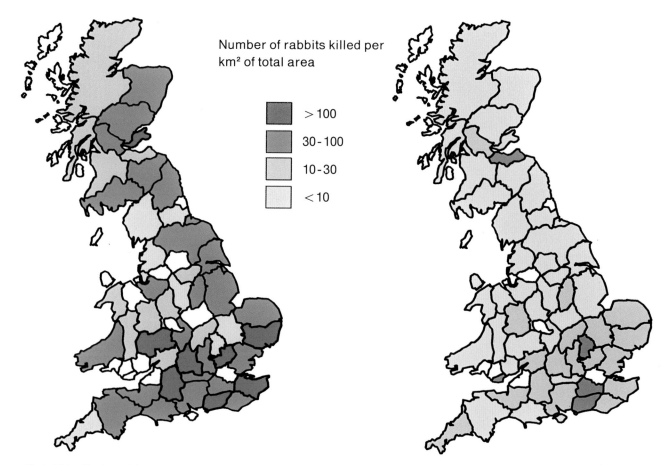

Number of rabbits killed per km² of total area

> 100

30 - 100

10 - 30

< 10

Fig 2.1 Distribution of the average bag of rabbits between 1900 and 1938.

Fig 2.2 Distribution of the average bag of rabbits between 1961 and 1985.

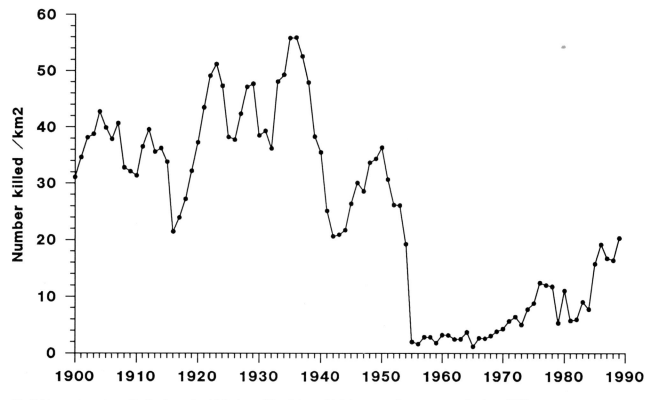

Fig 2.3 Long-term trend in the bag of rabbits from 63 estates which have continuous records since 1900.

Interpretation of the bag record since the turn of the century is affected by the changing nature of rabbit control and by the manner in which rabbit numbers have been recorded. Thus in the early part of the 20th century estate records are often a composite of what is taken on shooting days, by gamekeepers during normal shooting and trapping activities, and also by rabbit catchers. Such recording has not always been consistent and records do not usually present a picture of all animals killed on the estate as complete as for most game species. Thus the numbers killed per unit area can only be regarded as a minimum. Furthermore it is likely that the basis for the data collection changed after myxomatosis; rabbit catchers lost their jobs and control and any recording might have passed to the local Rabbit Clearance Societies. Thus Figs 2.1 and 2.2 are not directly comparable, but they do indicate the massive reduction in bag that has taken place. Fig 2.1 is very similar to a density distribution map shown by Thompson & Worden (1956). However, Cornwall appears to be seriously underestimated in the distribution of the bag.

Changes in numbers of rabbits killed each year prior to myxomatosis were not always random and although rabbits are not as quasi-cyclic as hares or grouse (see Appendix II), some series do show a weak 8 or 12 year quasi-cycle (Fig 2.5; Tapper, 1987).

The disease myxomatosis is caused by the *Myxoma* virus. It was originally isolated from American cottontail rabbits where it is not a serious form of natural mortality. Its lethality to European rabbits was only discovered when laboratory animals were accidentally infected. The virus introduced to Australia and continental Europe in 1950 and 1952 was the highly virulent Lusanne strain (Fenner & Chapple, 1965) and its effect on populations was devastating. Introduction to Britain followed shortly and was probably undertaken by farmers as an efficient form of pest control. The epidemic started in Edenbridge in Kent in October 1953 and is believed to have come from populations in France. Thompson & Worden (1956) give a detailed account of this early phase of the outbreak. Within a short period it had spread across the whole of the United Kingdom. This first wave killed 99.9% of all rabbits in its passing.

The changes in rabbit abundance that have taken place since 1954 can only be understood if they are seen as a reflection of evolutionary changes that have taken place not only in the *Myxoma* virus but in the rabbits themselves. In Britain the virus is transmitted from one animal to another by the rabbit flea—a particularly suitable vector since its own breeding is timed to coincide exactly with the rabbit's reproductive cycle (Mead-Briggs & Rudge, 1960). The importance of the flea as a vector was not clearly understood at first and as a result many early attempts to establish the virus from dead and dying rabbits failed. It normally takes 10-12 days for a rabbit to build up sufficient virus in its blood for host fleas to become infective carriers (Mead-Briggs & Vaughan, 1975). The early strains, although virulent, killed the animal too quickly and few fleas became infective. Less virulent strains which allowed rabbits to have a longer infective period had a considerable selective advantage and therefore became the predominant types in British rabbits in the 1960's (Fenner & Chapple, 1965; Ross, 1972). However these less virulent strains also allowed some rabbits to recover. Once recovered, an animal will retain its immunity (Vaughan & Vaughan, 1968) and a female can pass on temporary immunity to its offspring while nursing. Along with this attenuation of the virus there is now clear evidence that rabbits are becoming genetically resistant to the disease (Ross & Saunders, 1984). These effects are undoubtedly responsible for the increase in rabbit bags that have taken place nationally (Fig 2.4), regionally (Fig 2.6), and locally (Fig 2.7) in the 1960's and 1970's. There appears to have been a steady rate of increase (Fig 2.7), and with hindsight the general view that rabbits were not significantly increasing in the 1960's and early 1970's was erroneous. Nevertheless, recent experiments clearly demonstrate that myxomatosis still reduces rabbit abundance (Trout, Ross, & Fox, 1991).

Of all the changes in abundance described in this book the impact which myxomatosis has had on rabbits is the most dramatic, and it has had far reaching effects on the countryside as whole (Sumption & Flowerdew, 1985). The future of rabbit abundance is still open to speculation, and evidence as to whether they are continuing to increase is still contradictory (Trout, Tapper, & Harradine, 1986).

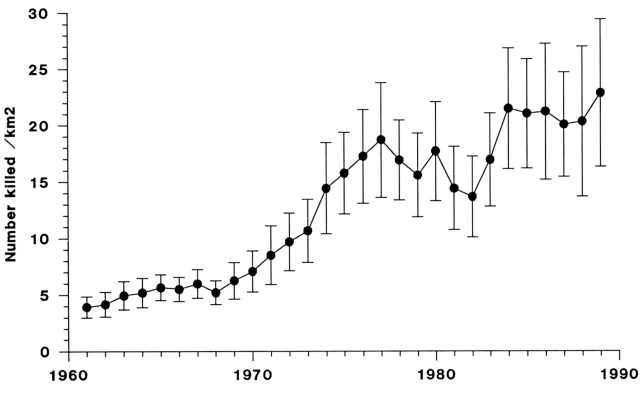

Fig 2.4 Trend in the average bag of rabbits since 1961.

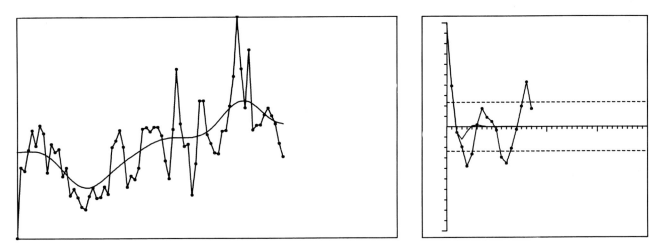

Fig 2.5 Time series analysis of pre-war rabbit bags from a Norfolk estate (from Middleton, 1934). Square root of the annual bag (left) and correlogram (right). See Appendix II for an explanation of time series analysis.

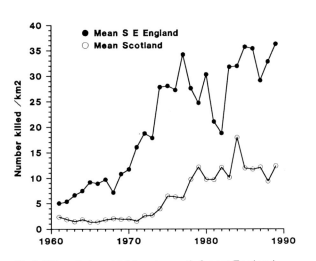

Fig 2.6 Trends in rabbit bag in south & east England compared to Scotland.

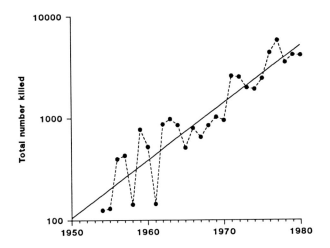

Fig 2.7 Logarithmic trend in rabbits killed on a Sussex downland shoot. This shows a more or less straight line increase, indicating that rabbit populations have had a steady rate of recovery ever since myxomatosis in 1954.

Brown Hare *(Lepus europaeus)*

The brown hare is the most widely pursued small game species in Europe. In Britain, although not esteemed for shooting, it is a precious quarry for a wide range of field sports—notably hare coursing, and hare hunting with beagles. It is also the classic target for poachers, particularly those with greyhounds or cross-bred lurchers. Nevertheless, hares are also considered agricultural pests and the Ground Game Act (1880) allows farmers to take them at any time of the year to protect crops. However, the Hare Preservation Act (1892) prevents the sale of hares between March and July inclusive.

This wide range of people killing hares inevitably means that the numbers recorded in game-books do not always reflect the total bag. For example, on a large estate some hares will be taken on partridge or pheasant shooting days and these will almost certainly be entered in the game book. However, in some instances gamekeepers may be allowed take a few hares as an employee's perk and these may or may not be recorded. Tenant farmers, having the legal right to kill hares, could also take a few and it is unlikely that these will get recorded in either the game book or on any National Game Bag Census return form which might be sent to The Game Conservancy in the spring. If the estate organises an annual hare shoot most tenant farmers will probably leave their hare shooting until then. Hare shoot totals usually do get entered into game books, but because they are often held rather late in the season (i.e. February or March) they may get left off our census form total, sometimes being added to the next season's return. Hares hunted by beagles or hares coursed are unlikely to get recorded in game books.

Hare shoots on arable farms are usually organised on the "Kesselring" principle. Between 20 and 40 guns are employed, generally made up of farmers, farm workers, gamekeepers and members of the shooting syndicate. These people surround a block of land of 100 to 200 hectares (250 to 500 acres) and gradually move inwards, shooting hares as they try to escape from the contract-

ing circle. Such hare shoots are a very effective, if sometimes hazardous, method of short-term control, since they can remove a high proportion of the hare stock (Barnes & Tapper, 1985) at a time of the year when hares are generally feeding on the new winter corn (Tapper & Barnes, 1986).

Brown hares are animals of the open steppe that have adapted well to man's arable farming systems. They are not native to Britain as is the mountain hare and probably came with the Romans (Corbet, 1986). Over much of Europe their spread was associated with forest clearance and the development of agriculture. This process has even taken place in recent times; Corbet (1986) shows that until the early 19th century their eastern range was limited by the Urals, but since then they have gradually pushed across Russia with the building of the trans-Siberian railway and its associated forest clearance. Unlike most other farmland game, which relies on the interstitial habitats such as hedgerows for its survival, hares breed in open fields and can thrive on mixed arable farms with no woodland or hedge. However, ground cover is essential, particularly for leverets, to avoid predation. This probably explains why hares are much more abundant in arable counties where cereals and other crops provide summer cover (Figs 3.1 & 3.2), than in districts where upland and lowland pasture predominate and cover is sparse. Brown hares are also absent from extensive areas of heather moor, and in Scotland are replaced by the mountain hare which can feed off heather shoots. Figs 3.1 & 3.2 show that larger numbers of hares were shot in the pre-war era than post 1961. Fig 3.3 indicates what was probably the changing level of hare abundance in the arable areas of south and eastern England. Bags were highest in the early part of the century; after the late twenties they declined until the latter half of the Second World War. The significance of this is not clear but there was a growing agricultural depression until the war, and with fewer cereals hares may have had less food and cover—indicating a real decrease in abundance. Low

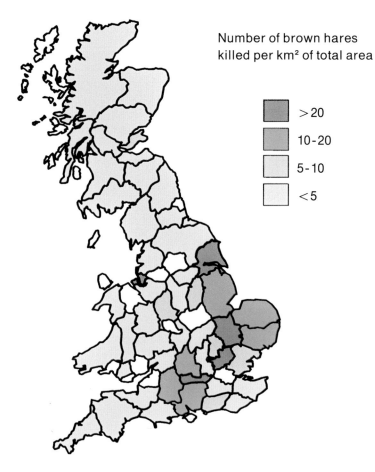

Number of brown hares
killed per km² of total area

> 20

10-20

5-10

< 5

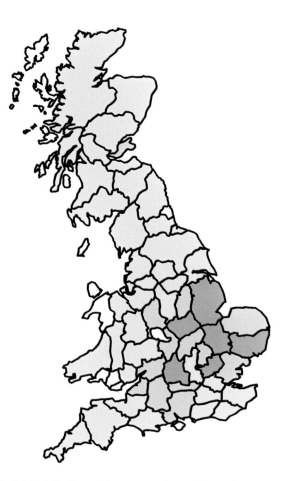

Fig 3.1 Distribution of the average bag of brown hares
between 1900 and 1938.

Fig 3.2 Distribution of the average bag of brown hares
between 1961 and 1985.

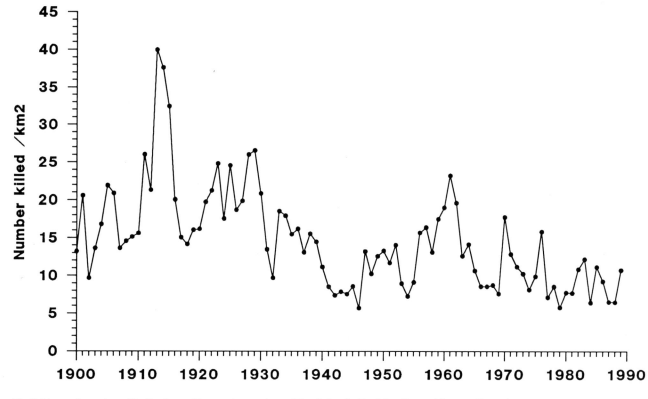

Fig 3.3 Long-term trend in the bag of brown hares from 12 estates in East Anglia and the south east.

numbers during the wars are less likely to represent real decreases and may be due either to a lack of shooting or to an increasing proportion being taken by tenant farmers during periods when meat was scarce.

The post-war numbers show an increase until 1960 and a decline over the last two decades. The decline since 1960 is more marked in the national trend (Fig 3.4) than in the long-term series, but it is shown in virtually all regions. Tapper & Parsons (1984) concluded that it represented a real decrease in abundance and that the bag was reducing at a more or less steady rate when considered nationally. This pattern appears to be similar to changes that have taken place in other European countries (Fig 3.5). In Sweden, hares increased after their introduction in 1886 but have declined since 1950 (Frylestam, 1976). In Denmark, bags are well recorded and there was an increase between 1902 and 1944 (Andersen, 1957) but a decline since 1957 (Strandgaard & Asferg, 1980). Recent declines have also been recorded in the Netherlands (Broekhuizen, 1981), Switzerland (Salzmann-Wandeler, 1976), West Germany and Austria (Anon, 1991), and parts of France (Fiechter & Bemmergui, 1986). Much research on hares has been directed towards finding the cause of these reductions.

It is possible that these downward trends are caused by natural ecological changes. The weather, for example, is correlated with annual variation in the bag and high numbers are associated with mild springs (Andersen, 1957; Barnes & Tapper, 1986). An increased pregnancy rate and a larger than average litter size are associated with mild springs (Flux, 1967; Frylestam, 1980). Mild autumns appear to lengthen the breeding season, and in Scotland Hewson & Taylor (1975) found the season varied between 176 and 344 days in different years. Post-war changes might be related to the huge reduction in rabbits through myxomatosis—a factor which was noted at the time (Moore, 1956; Rothschild & Marsh, 1956). Barnes & Tapper (1986) tried to sort out these factors using a multiple regression model to predict post-war changes based on pre-war data (see Fig 3.6). They concluded that there had been a boom in hare numbers in the late 1950's and early 1960's as a consequence of the myxomatosis epizootic in rabbits. But this, and a series of poor breeding seasons did not provide an adequate explanation of the decline since. They also pointed out that the trend in bag from Denmark was remarkably similar to the trend in Britain and yet rabbits are virtually absent from Denmark.

The search for a complete explanation has centred on the changing farming scene over the last two decades, and increasing levels of predation. Tapper & Barnes (1986) concluded that the relentless simplification of arable systems was a major factor. Although there is plenty of correlative evidence for this in terms of habitat use by hares, their distribution in autumn, and temporal changes within farms (Tapper & Barnes, 1986), as yet no clear cut biological mechanism has been put forward. Frylestam's (1979) finding that in some areas of arable monoculture in Sweden, hares were underweight in summer and that breeding performance was reduced offers a likely avenue for future research. Also relevant is the fact that fox numbers appear to have increased over a similar time span, and where fox numbers have been reduced by rabies or anti-rabies campaigns, increases in the hare bag have been noted (Strandgaard & Asferg, 1980; Pegel, 1986). The same has been seen where foxes have been reduced experimentally (Tapper, Potts & Brockless, 1991).

Most of the variation in the bag between years appears to be the result of the random influence of the weather. However, data from some estates do show cyclic changes with an average length between peaks of about 8 years—Fig 3.7 (Middleton, 1934; Tapper, 1987). When estate records are taken together from a number of places the presence of this 8 year cycle is clearly significant, even though we still have no clear explanation as to what might cause it.

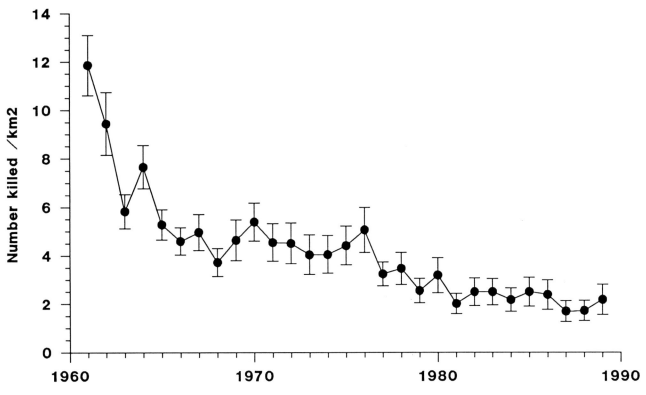

Fig 3.4 Trend in the average bag of brown hares since 1961.

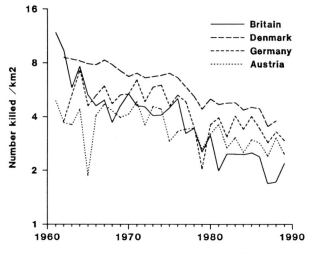

Fig 3.5 Changing rates of decline of the brown hare bag in four west European countries. Bag per 100 hectares on a logarithmic scale. Continental data from, Strandgaard & Asferg (1980) and Anon (1991).

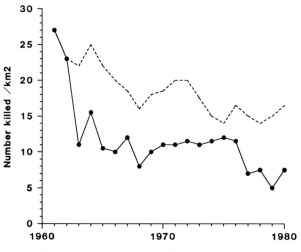

Fig 3.6 The bag of brown hares in East Anglia (solid line) compared to predictions from a multiple regression weather model (dashed line) calculated from pre-war East Anglian bags and assuming identical values to start in 1961. For details of the model see Barnes & Tapper (1986).

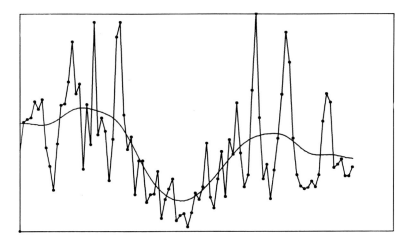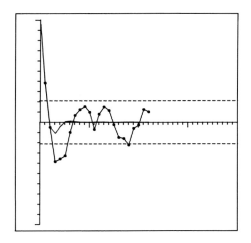

Fig 3.7 Time-series and correlogram of brown hare bags from a Yorkshire estate showing an 8 year quasi-cycle. (See Appendix II for an explanation of time-series analysis).

Mountain Hare *(Lepus timidus)*

In Britain the mountain or blue hare is an upland species—typically found on high heather moorland, along with birds like the red grouse or ptarmigan. However, it is really a northern rather than a mountain species and in Scandinavia the same hare is found throughout the open tundra and boreal forest zones and is only replaced by the brown hare on southern farmlands. Interestingly, in Canada there are three separate species which occupy these same zones, the Arctic hare, the snowshoe hare and the jackrabbit, found in tundra, boreal and prairie regions respectively.

In Britain the mountain hare is a true native and it probably either remained here through the last ice age or came across the Channel land bridge as the ice sheet retreated (Corbet, 1986). Mountain hares may well have colonised a wider range of habitats as the climate ameliorated, and may only have been pushed to the uplands when the brown hares arrived with the Roman invasion. In Ireland the Irish hare (the same species as the mountain hare) is widespread and is found in lowland habitats as well. The mountain hare is indigenous to the Scottish Highlands, but today it is also found in the Borders, the Peak District and North Wales as a result of extensive introductions in the mid to late 19th century (Hewson, 1991). The Isle of Man population came from a later 20th century introduction (Fargher, 1977). The game bag in the pre and post war periods reflects this distribution (Figs 4.1 & 4.2), although these hares seem less abundant in most districts now than pre-war. Also, eastern counties have more hares than those in the west.

The lower numbers now being shot in the Peak District also reflect fewer hares, and a significant contraction of range in that population has occurred due to loss of heather through overgrazing (Andersen & Yalden, 1981). This is similar to the reduction in red grouse which has also occurred there (Hudson, 1986a). However, within the areas of good habitat numbers certainly increased again until the mid 1970's (Yalden, 1984) and there now appear to be about 1000 animals in the autumn. Nevertheless severe winters can knock the Peak District population back substantially and to that extent it can be considered vulnerable

On moorland in Scotland the traditional methods of heather management for grouse, a burning pattern which produces a patchwork of different aged plants, combined with intensive predator control, give ideal conditions for mountain hares. Densities of over 300 per 100 hectares are found on some moors (Watson & Hewson, 1973) even though the breeding season of mountain hares is shorter and their overall production lower than in brown hares (Hewson, 1964). Thus, it is not surprising that the trends of bag records for mountain hares parallel those of red grouse (Figs 4.3 & 4.4). High numbers were shot around the turn of the century and even more after the First World War. The low numbers during the Second World War were followed by a recovery to levels some 50% of those of the 1930's by 1950. There was a decline which lasted from the mid 1970's to the early 1980's but numbers have recovered substantially since (Fig 4.4).

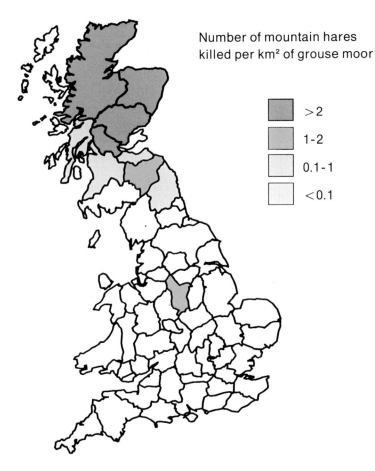

Number of mountain hares
killed per km² of grouse moor

▮ >2
▮ 1-2
▯ 0.1-1
▯ <0.1

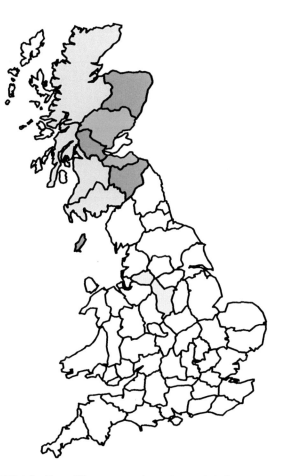

Fig 4.1 Distribution of the average bag of mountain hares between 1900 and 1938.

Fig 4.2 Distribution of the average bag of mountain hares between 1961 and 1985.

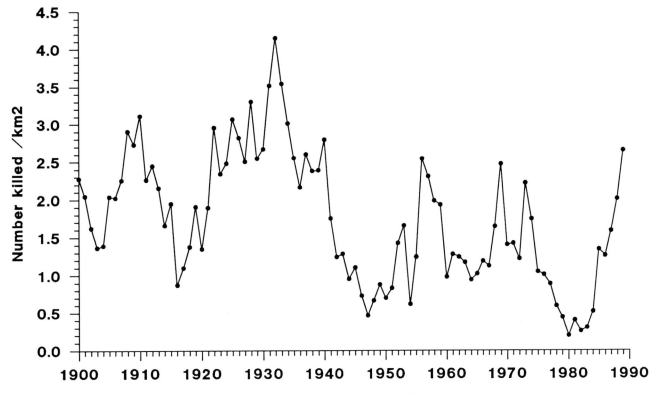

Fig 4.3 Long-term trend in the numbers of mountain hares shot on 44 moors in Scotland.

The high densities that mountain hares achieve on grouse moors, and the fact that they eat similar aged heather plants to red grouse means that they are often seen as grouse competitors. Also in some areas they are seen as reservoirs of 'louping ill'—the serious tick borne disease which affects sheep, grouse, and hares. For these reasons hare shoots are organised primarily as pest control measures. These shoots are usually gamekeeper and hill farmers' shoots rather than events attended by the moor owners or shooting tenants, so numbers killed may not be recorded in game books and the average bags should be regarded only as indicators of the true totals. Many hares are also killed by keepers throughout the year for dog food. However, there is increasing interest in hare shoots, particularly from visiting continental hunters who regard hares as a highly desirable sporting quarry. Flux (1970) described the operation on one Aberdeenshire shoot. On a hill of 260 hectares (640 acres), two shoots were organised with 25 guns on the first day and 30 on the second. Since mountain hares run uphill when disturbed, the drives were organised with guns starting off round the base of the hill and gradually walking upwards towards the summit; driving the hares before them and shooting them as they tried to escape. In this way 500 were killed on one day and 100 the next, probably removing over 90% of the population. However, it is likely that most hare shoots take nothing like this proportion and 10 to 50% is probably more typical. Being ranked rather low in the sporting scale, the planning and extent of hare shoots is not as carefully adjusted to the autumn stock as it is in red grouse, so results from individual moors may reflect only rough changes in hare density.

In spite of the obviously poorer level of recording and management of mountain hares compared with red grouse, some series do show that numbers are cyclic (Fig 4.5). Tapper (1987) in an analysis of hare bags from 20 Scottish grouse moors found that 9 showed evidence of weak quasi-cycles. The wave length varied between 4 and 12 years, and Fig 4.6 shows that when all 20 series were taken as a whole there was as an average cycle length of 9.5 years. This cycle in hares is longer than in red grouse where the typical length in Scotland is 6 years (Williams, 1985; Hudson & Dobson, 1990).

In seeking a cause of these cycles it is tempting to look for parallels with other cyclic hares such the Canadian snowshoe or the Scandinavian varying hare. However, these populations occupy a boreal habitat and their cycles appear to be fundamentally different in nature. The snowshoe hare cycle represents a phase-remembering rather than a phase-forgetting quasi-cycle of 10 years which is synchronous over a wide area (Keith, 1963; Finerty, 1980), and appears to be caused by an interaction of food shortage and predation (Keith et al., 1977). In Scandinavia the cycle is shorter (about 4 years) and is closely allied to the lemming cycle through a chain of linking predators (Lindstrom et al., 1986). Predators are normally strictly controlled on grouse moors so they are unlikely to play a major role in Scottish hare population cycles. Also, the lack of synchrony with red grouse numbers implies that the two species are not bound up in the same process, as are the north American hares and grouse. As yet no explanation of these cycles has been put forward. Given the level at which some populations are shot, it is entirely feasible that shooting itself could be an important factor.

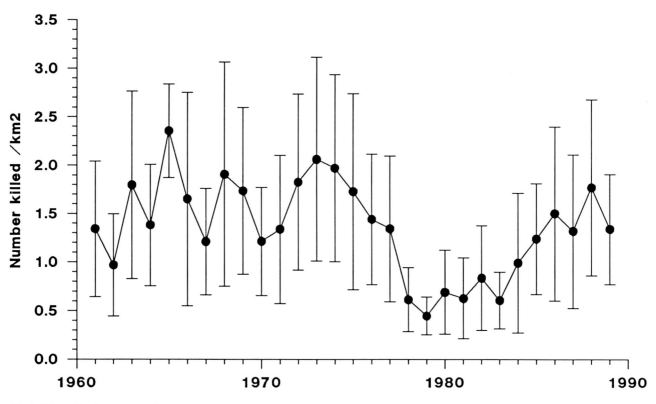

Fig 4.4 Trend in the average bag of mountain hares since 1961.

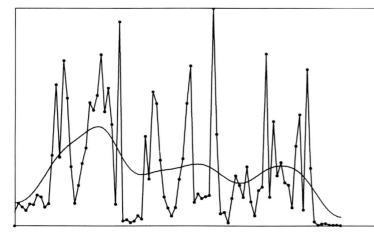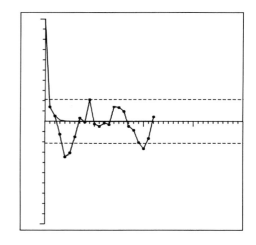

Fig 4.5 Time series analysis of mountain hare bags from a Scottish estate.

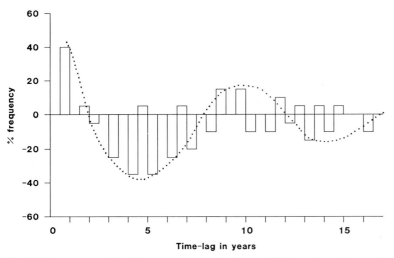

Fig 4.6 Frequency of significant auto-correlation coefficients from the analysis of 20 series with more than 30 years of data. Indicating a cycle length of about 9 years. (See Appendix II for details of time-series analysis).

Woodpigeon *(Columba palumbus)*

Pigeons are often regarded as the poor man's gamebird. This is because, as an agricultural pest, most pigeon shooting is left to the farmers who enlist their own employees, or a third party willing to help protect farm crops in exchange for free shooting. Pigeons are not always entered in game books and many contributors to the census do not keep a full total of all those shot, so actual numbers killed are likely to be much higher than those shown in our records.

The pigeon shooter's normal approach is a careful reconnaissance to decide where the birds are feeding and to locate their flight lines to and from roosting trees. A strategy is then developed to intercept them as they fly in to feed. A concealed hide is often used, usually made of camouflage netting, natural vegetation or sometimes straw bales, and decoys are put out to attract birds within shooting range. In this way a large number can be killed by a single person—on one occasion 550 in a day (Coats, 1963). Birds may also be shot at the wood as they come into roost.

Pigeons appear to have become more numerous over the 20th century as a result of farming improvements, and the few long-term data sets tend to support this (Fig 5.5). In the past they probably relied on weed seeds and stubble gleanings, and their numbers were limited by lack of winter forage such as acorns and mast. However, with the introduction of ley farming and new crops like clover, kale, and fodder rape, their overwinter survival must have increased, giving rise a higher pigeon population. Today, arable farmland is the primary habitat of this species and this is reflected in the geographical variation in the bag, with a heavy preponderance in eastern and south eastern regions (Fig 5.1).

The changing abundance since the early 1960's reflects mainly changes in farming. However, severely cold winter weather aggravates foraging conditions for pigeons because crops stop growing and the bird's energy needs increase. This adds to crop damage and the need for pigeon control. When crops are buried in snow many pigeons starve to death. This was most noticeable in the 1962/3 winter when large numbers of emaciated birds were found dead and dying all over the country, a situation that was exacerbated by the presence of dieldrin seed dressings on much of the winter corn (Jefferies & Presst, 1966). That winter must have reduced pigeon numbers substantially and the bag records, both nationally (Fig 5.2) and in the eastern region (Fig 5.3) suggest that it took about six years for populations to recover.

From the late 1960's to the mid 1970's bags were declining. During this period pigeon numbers appear to have been regulated mainly by food supply during the late winter and early spring (Murton, 1965; Murton, Isaacson & Westwood, 1966). The key to the birds' survival was clover, providing the only food source available to them before the spring drilling. The gradual decline in ley farming and in mixed arable livestock systems, and a shift towards specialised all cereal farms, substantially reduced the winter food for pigeons. This probably accounts for the decline in bags between 1969 and 1976 (Figs 5.2 & 5.3). The reversal since then appears to be entirely due to a relatively new crop, oilseed rape.

Oilseed rape was first introduced into arable systems during the late 1960's, and since then there has been a wide expansion of the crop, with uptake on a large scale (Fig 5.4). Initially most crops were spring sown and did not benefit pigeons much, but the development of high yielding winter varieties caused most farmers to switch to winter sowings. These fields proved ideal feeding areas for pigeons in the critical late winter/ spring period (Inglis, Threarle & Isaacson, 1989). It appears that the increasing rape area is now allowing the woodpigeon population to offset the loss of clover, and while the oilseed acreage continues to expand we can expect pigeon numbers to rise as well. Certainly they seem to do better on oilseed rape than they ever did on clover, and recent data show they no longer lose weight overwinter and that their survival is improved (Inglis *et al.*, 1990). This is likely to lead to much higher levels of shooting to reduce damage, particularly during cold winters.

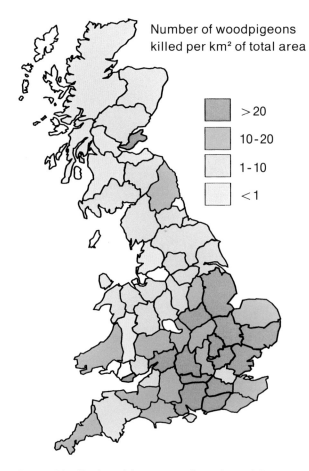

Number of woodpigeons killed per km² of total area

> 20

10 - 20

1 - 10

< 1

Fig 5.1 Distribution of the average bag of woodpigeons between 1961 and 1985.

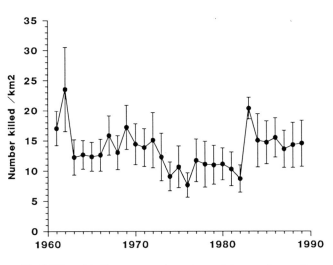

Fig 5.2 Trend in the average bag of woodpigeons from all Britain since 1961.

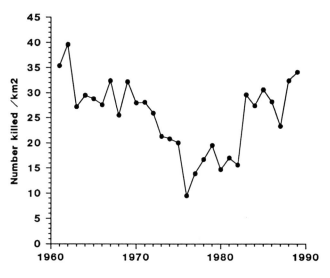

Fig 5.3 Numbers of woodpigeons shot in East Anglia since 1961.

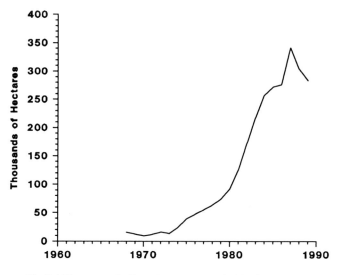

Fig 5.4 The area of oilseed rape grown in England since 1968. From Ministry of Agriculture June returns.

Fig 5.5 Numbers of woodpigeons killed on a Suffolk estate since they were first recorded in 1916. The sharp increase since the mid 1950's partly reflects an increased area of arable taken in as a consequence of the near disappearance of rabbits after myxomatosis.

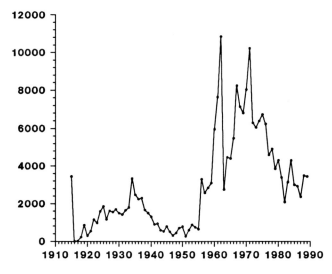

Grey Partridge *(Perdix perdix)*

Driven game shooting on farmland was primarily organised around the grey partridge, and during the 19th century their numbers increased for three main reasons. First, the agricultural revolution led to an increasing acreage of cereals, which provided a grass prairie habitat to which partridges were well adapted. Second, land enclosure, with its associated increase in hedgerow, gave good nesting cover, largely undisturbed by livestock and human interference. Thirdly, in order to protect poultry, rabbit warrens, gamebirds, and other livestock, most predators were subjected to increasing eradication campaigns, which must have substantially increased nesting success. By the turn of the century partridge stocks and shooting bags had risen to very high levels, and driven partridge shooting had become a highly fashionable pastime.

On most estates the aims of partridge management have changed little since these times, and the methods described by Maxwell (1911) still provide a standard to which many landowners aspire—even though under modern conditions they can almost never be achieved. Maxwell's optimum was to have a large estate of about 8000 acres (3200 hectares—preferably adjacent to others where similar management was being practised), divided into partridge beats of between 800 to 1500 acres (320 to 600 hectares). On each beat an underkeeper was responsible for protecting the partridge stock and destroying the vermin. He was also expected to find the majority of partridge nests, and to check them daily—taking action should any predator kill the hen or remove the eggs. Even though the predator control Maxwell advocated might appear ruthless by present day standards, he did emphasise that it should be selective, and he very much regretted the unnecessary killing of raptors that had been widespread in the 19th century. Although Maxwell appreciated the importance of adequate nesting cover and realised, even then, that chick survival was very dependent on insect abundance, he devoted almost no space in his book to these aspects. It is clear that these requirements were largely fulfilled on Edwardian farms, and the real problem was one of predator control.

In areas where foxes were preserved for hunting the Euston system of nest management was developed. This involved removing the eggs from under the hen at the start of incubation and replacing them with dummy eggs. The real ones were then reared under bantams in the safety of the rearing field, and when incubation was complete the eggs were replaced under a sitting hen partridge at the time of chipping. By returning eggs to different parents it was possible to shorten the period any hen was sitting by as much as a week, and to provide a female with up to 30 chipping eggs. This was important, since many hens would inevitably be lost though fox predation. It is often claimed that the Euston system enabled good partridge bags to be had from counties where hunting was the primary interest. However it is far from clear that this system ever worked to a large extent (Potts, 1986), and it may be that even in hunting counties sufficient fox control was exerted in the summer to prevent serious hen losses.

Using traditional methods in a sympathetic landscape, partridge management gave good returns not only in the eastern counties but throughout much of the midlands and southern Britain as well (Fig 6.1). The long-term bag record (Fig 6.3) indicates that numbers were maintained at a high level until the outbreak of the Second World War, in spite of the growing unprofitability of cereal production. Bags were highly variable between years, with the good ones being two or three times the low years. This exaggerated actual variation in production, since landowners always conserved stocks after poor breeding seasons and greatly restricted or cancelled shooting following such years. The number shot is related to autumn stock, and the relationship between the two can be described with a logistic curve (Potts, 1980). Following the Second World War partridge management was only partially restored before numbers collapsed on an unprecedented scale in the early 1950's (Fig 6.3). Since then partridge shooting has been a mere shadow of former times (Fig 6.2).

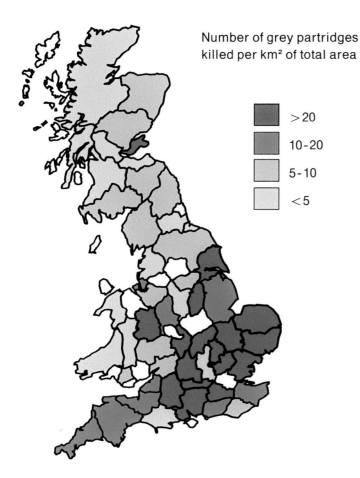

Number of grey partridges
killed per km² of total area

- ▨ > 20
- ▨ 10-20
- ▨ 5-10
- ▨ < 5

Fig 6.1 Distribution of the average bag of partridges between 1900 and 1938.

Fig 6.2 Distribution of the average bag of partridges between 1961 and 1985.

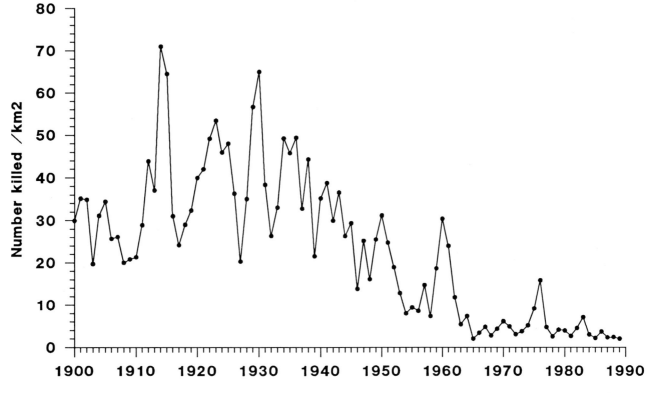

Fig 6.3 Long-term trend in the bag from 12 estates in East Anglia and south east England which have continuous records since 1900.

37

The decline of the grey partridge in Britain in the 1950's was not an isolated case and there is clear evidence that the same pattern of events occurred on a world-wide scale. Potts (1986) tabulates over twenty countries where the bag of this species dropped dramatically. Pre-war some 20 million partridges were being bagged annually, whereas in recent years it amounts to less than 3.8 million (Potts, 1986). This is the most serious loss of any game species yet recorded. The reasons for the decline are now well understood, even though it came at time of great environmental change in the countryside. Herbicides, insecticides and artificial fertilisers became prevalent in agriculture. Myxomatosis all but wiped out the commonest medium sized mammal, and set in train a series of unprecedented habitat changes in lowland Britain. In Europe game management and farming were still recovering from the havoc of the war.

Fortunately partridge research was well established in pre-war Britain, and a considerable fund of knowledge exists on pre-decline populations. Particularly, the technique of autumn counting coveys of young and old birds was well known, and Middleton (1936) presented 30 years of such data from Great Witchingham in Norfolk. Working for the forerunner of today's Game Conservancy he also established the levels of the key parameters of breeding success i.e. hen, egg, and chick survival. Luckily, chick diet was also investigated in detail (Ford, Chitty & Middleton, 1938), and the partridge's preference for insect food is well documented. After the war research was renewed by Blank & Ash (1954), who showed that a post war population could quickly be restored with sympathetic management (Fig 6.5). However, by the late 50's there were fears that herbicides might be affecting chick survival even though adverse weather was still felt to be primarily responsible for chick losses (Blank & Ash, 1957). There was something of a reprieve in 1959 and 1960 with good reproduction but after that breeding success dropped on the Game Conservancy's study area at Damerham and on other key estates (Ash, 1967). Nationally the shooting bags plummeted (Fig 6.4).

In the immediate post-war period there was an increasing amount of field research, but detailed analysis of the data was lacking and it wasn't until the late 1960's that a series of papers singled out the problem. The viability of eggs and their hatching success was good (Southwood, 1967), but chick survival was the key variable limiting breeding success on areas with keepers (Blank, Southwood & Cross, 1967), and when herbicides removed the food plants for the insects upon which these chicks depended, their survival was reduced (Southwood & Cross, 1969).

Although the introduction of herbicides triggered the decline, other factors played an increasing role in regulating partridge abundance on modern cereal farms (Potts & Vickerman, 1974). In particular, declines in the levels of gamekeeping increased losses to predators and the removal of hedgerows increased spring dispersal and caused reductions in spring stocks. Using a simulation model, Potts (1980) showed how all these factors combined to reduce abundance to the levels indicated by the National Game Bag Census (i.e. Fig 6.4).

In recent years investigations have centred on ways to increase chick survival so that steps can be taken to restore partridges in the remaining well managed habitats. Green (1984a) showed, by radio-tracking females with chicks, that broods preferred to forage around field edges. This has led to the new concept of reduced pesticide use along field margins (Sotherton, Boatman & Rands, 1989; Sotherton, 1991). These 'Conservation Headlands' have now been extensively researched by the Cereals and Gamebirds Project organised by Hugh Oliver-Bellasis. Under these minimum spray conditions, chick survival can be increased to pre-war levels (Rands, 1985). When combined with correct hedgerow management (Rands, 1986) and adequate protection from predators, a computer simulation model suggests that partridge numbers can be restored (Potts, 1986). However, as yet there is no sign that the introduction of these new methods has increased the overall bag.

Variation in shooting bags were large in the pre-war heyday, and although partridges have never been regarded as a cyclic species by landowners, and there is little in their biology which would suggest a mechanism, Middleton (1934) contended that they did show a 9 year cycle. Correlograms of bag records from individual estates reveal no clear cycle (Fig 6.7). But when the data from a number of places are combined, a weak cycle of about 9 to 10 years shows up (Fig 6.6). This cycle is much weaker and longer than the one we find in grouse, which appears to be caused by a recurrent parasite infection, so at the moment we have no adequate explanation for this phenomenon except that it is likely to result from some density dependant mortality factor acting with a time delay.

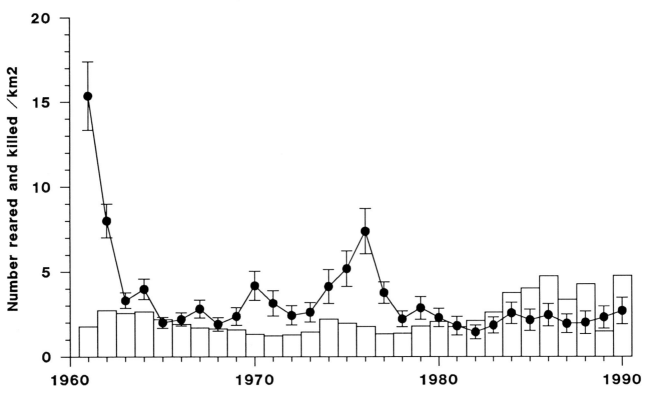

Fig 6.4 Trends in the average bag and the average number reared (open bars) of grey partridges since 1961.

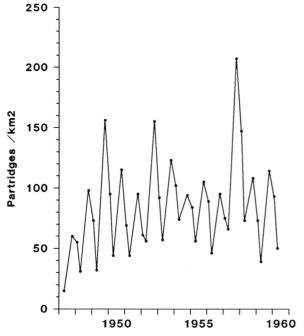

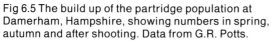

Fig 6.5 The build up of the partridge population at Damerham, Hampshire, showing numbers in spring, autumn and after shooting. Data from G.R. Potts.

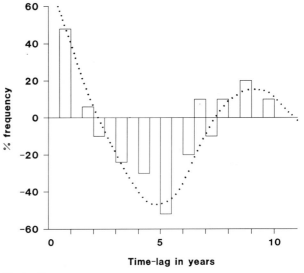

Fig 6.6 Frequency of significant auto-correlation coefficients from the analysis of 19 grey partridge series with more than 50 years of data. (See Appendix II for technical details).

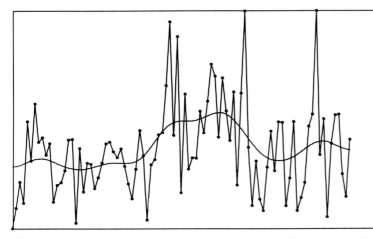

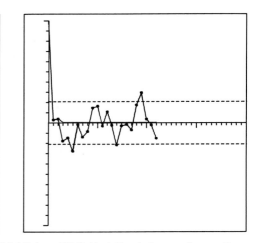

Fig 6.7 Time series analysis of a pre- war data from a Norfolk estate (from Middleton, 1934). Variation in bag and overall trend (left) and correlogram (right). (See Appendix II for technical details)

Redleg Partridge *(Alectoris rufa)*

Redlegs are not true native birds of Britain but were successfully introduced for shooting in the late 18th century. Earlier attempts appear to have failed. The exact date is not known but several landowners were involved, and by the end of the century they were well established. Lever (1977) has reviewed what we know of these early introductions, and it is clear that they were all taken from southern France and were the *Alectoris rufa rufa* sub-species, not the Spanish race *A. r. hispanica*. Other species of redleg, such as the chukar (*A. chukar*) have been introduced much later—mainly by game farmers in the 1960's and 1970's.

The true *A. rufa* have adapted to the wild and now thrive, particularly in East Anglia where they were first introduced, and this is reflected in the bag (Fig 7.1). So successful were they in fact, that there was some concern among sportsmen that they were pushing out the native grey partridge. However, this seems unlikely. A more probable scenario is suggested by Potts (1980). The redleg is a slower, lower flying bird, and tends to fly singly when driven over the guns. Thus, where greys are managed and shot intensively, redlegs are easily over-harvested and their stocks kept down. After the war, with the decline of the grey partridge due to the introduction of herbicides, many estates virtually ceased partridge shooting, thus allowing redleg numbers to build up proportionally. Furthermore, Green (1984a) found that redleg chicks we less dependent than grey partridge chicks on insect food during the first days of their lives, and they could digest grass and weed seeds soon after hatching. This makes them less vulnerable to the indirect effects of herbicides.

Although not affected by herbicides, redlegs did suffer with the decline of partridge management, and particularly the relaxation of predator control which followed an increasing emphasis on hand-reared pheasants. Potentially the redleg is a more prolific breeder than the grey, because a pair can lay two clutches which can be independently and simultaneously incubated by the hen and cock bird to give two broods (Green, 1984b).

However, the nests are not well hidden, and they are therefore exposed to higher rates of predation than the grey partridge. This is particularly true for the first clutch, of which the first egg may be laid more than a month before incubation begins. The net effect is that on unkeepered ground redlegs breed less well than greys.

The loss of wild partridge shooting encouraged many keepers and farmers to concentrate on hand reared birds. Keepers had often raised redlegs and grey partridges in small numbers, and when larger numbers of partridges were required the redleg proved to be a more straightforward bird to rear than the grey. Further, reared grey partridges had the tendency to pack up into enormous flocks like starlings which made sensible driven shooting impossible. Reared redlegs, on the other hand, would remain in coveys if released from small temporary pens put out onto stubble fields. However, in the late 1960's game farmers started experimenting with chukars and redleg x chukar hybrids. These birds made excellent game farm birds, since they could easily be flock mated and the hens laid almost twice as many eggs. The consequence has been that during the 1970's the proportion of shoots releasing partridges has increased (Fig 7.3), and the average number of birds they put down has soared (Fig 7.4). The net result is a rising national bag increasingly dependent on an input of reared birds (Fig 7.2). These hybrid birds are usually regarded as a put and take game crop rather than as a reinforcement to an existing wild stock. Thus releasing has not been restricted to the normal range of the wild bird and now takes place through much of lowland Britain (Fig 7.5). This has increased the distribution of redleg types in the bag, but the breeding performance of hybrids in the wild is negligible and there is good evidence that where they are mixed with wild redlegs the resulting hybridisation leads to a deterioration of the wild stock. The release of partridges other than *A. rufa* or *Perdix perdix* was banned under the Wildlife and Countryside Act 1981 and the rearing of hybrids and chukars is being phased out, ceasing in 1992.

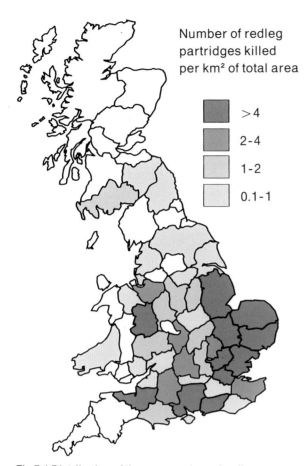

Fig 7.1 Distribution of the average bag of redleg partridges between 1961 and 1985.

Number of redleg partridges killed per km² of total area

- >4
- 2-4
- 1-2
- 0.1-1

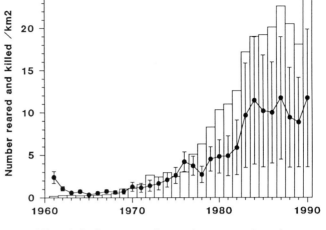

Fig 7.2 Trends in the average bag and mean number of redleg partridges released (open bars) from all Britain since 1961.

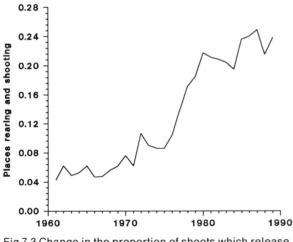

Fig 7.3 Change in the proportion of shoots which release redleg partridges.

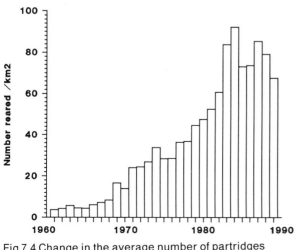

Fig 7.4 Change in the average number of partridges released per 100 hectares.

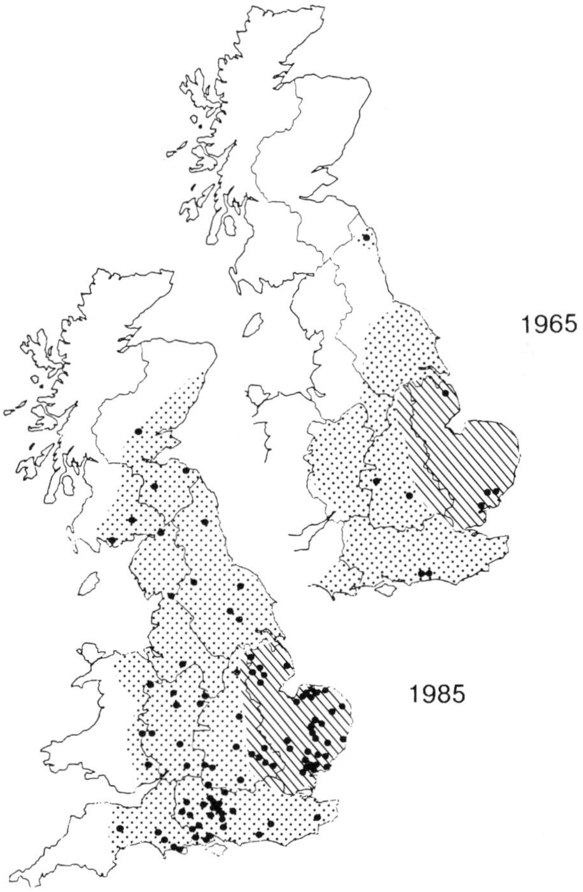

1965

1985

Fig 7.5 Shoots contributing to the National Game Bag Census that released more than 50 redlegs (black dot); the region where significant numbers of wild birds are shot (hatched); and the area where redlegs are recorded in the bag (stipple).

41

Pheasant *(Phasianus colchicus)*

The pheasant has become the most important gamebird in Britain. Although there are no accurate figures available, it is possible to estimate the total bag by using National Game Bag Census figures in relation to the total land area, and the proportion of it which is shot over (from Piddington, 1981). This gives an estimate of 12 million birds shot, derived in part from 20 million which are hand-reared each year. This has come about as much through the decline of wild species like the grey partridge, as it has through the simplicity of modern artificial propagation. The tractability of the pheasant to hand-rearing has allowed gamekeepers to adapt the new technology of poultry science to raising gamebirds.

Pheasants are not native birds, and it was originally thought that they were brought to Britain in Roman times, because illustrations of pheasants have been found in Romano-British mosaics. However, these pictures do not necessarily imply that pheasants were feral locally, indeed in some cases the mosaics show a ring-necked bird which is different from the original Old English *(Phasianus colchicus colchicus)* which has no ring and is commonly referred to as a black-neck. Thus recent thinking is that our pheasants came with the Normans, probably from stock derived from the Caucasus region of central Asia (Hill & Robertson, 1988). The bird was probably quite common by Tudor times and abundant in the 19th century, by which time landowners were experimenting to try to improve the "blood" of their local stock using other breeds such as the Japanese green *(P.c. versicolor)*, the Chinese ring neck *(P.c. torquatus)*, and the Mongolian *(P.c. mongolicus)*, as well as various crosses (Johnsgard, 1986). It is now difficult to know exactly what the original bird looked like. However, on some Norfolk estates and in fenland districts, where few birds are reared, the wild pheasants have the Old English appearance and are smaller than other typical hand-reared stock (1200 grams as opposed to 1450 grams for males and 860 grams as opposed to 1100 grams for females—Peter Robertson, pers. comm.). These birds may well be similar to the ones that came to Britain in medieval times.

The rearing system employed during the 19th and the first half of the 20th century was based on using farmyard hens as foster parents. Eggs were produced from pheasants caught up from the coverts and taken into special laying pens, or from birds kept permanently in aviaries. Alternatively some estate owners relied on collecting eggs from early nests laid in the wild, on the premise that the hen would always lay again. This latter system gained a bad reputation, as it led to a considerable egg trade and many landowners were duped into buying eggs which had probably been stolen off their own ground (Tegetmeier, 1881; Turner, 1954). The pheasant eggs were set under broody hens many of which were often purchased from surrounding villages (Mursell, 1981). Once hatched, the broods were commonly taken to a large rearing field where lines of coops contained the hens, each with about 10 young pheasants. Looking after such a system was very labour intensive. At Elveden (an estate of 20,000 acres) 22 men were employed in the game department (Turner, 1954), and in spite of the low wages paid to keepers and farm workers, rearing pheasants was expensive. At the turn of the century each bird reared was worth approximately double a keepers weekly wage. Today a reared pheasant before release is worth only 1% of the modern wage.

As the young pheasants matured they were taken to the woods and held in the coverts by means of regular feeding along specific feed rides. A few of the hens often accompanied the pheasants and were thought to prevent birds from straying. In spite of this hand-rearing, wild birds constituted the major proportion of the bag on most shoots. Many estates, particularly in eastern counties, were able to sustain pheasant shoots without artificial rearing. So we must conclude that most hand-rearing before the second war was primarily to top up wild production and ensure that poor spring weather did not mean a disastrous season But it was recognised quite early on that artificial rearing had shortcomings and indeed Simpson (1903) argued that it should be abandoned altogether and that sympathetic forest management was a better way to produce more wild pheasants.

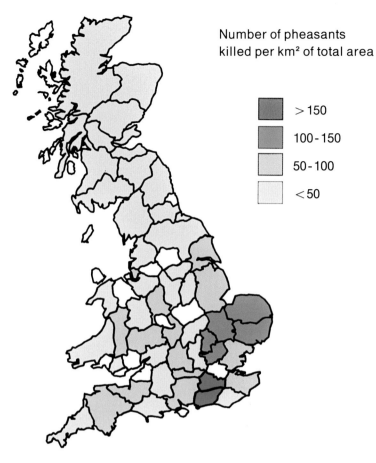

Number of pheasants
killed per km² of total area

> 150

100 - 150

50 - 100

< 50

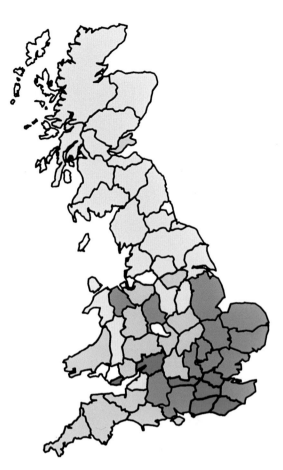

Fig 8.1 Distribution of the average bag of pheasants between 1900 and 1938.

Fig 8.2 Distribution of the average bag of pheasants between 1961 and 1985.

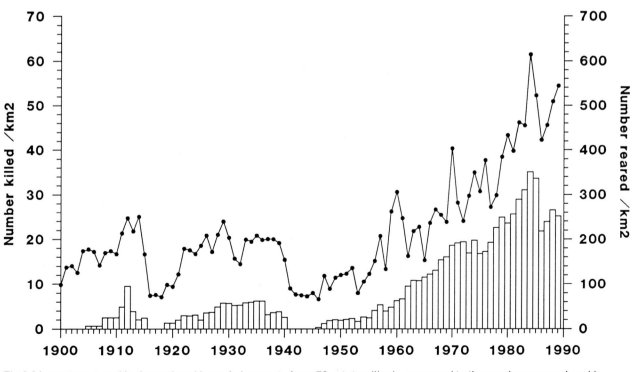

Fig 8.3 Long-term trend in the national bag of pheasants from 72 estates (line), compared to the numbers reared on 11 lowland estates where complete rearing records were kept (bar chart).

During both world wars and during periods of food rationing, game rearing virtually ceased. But the 1950's saw new methods of mass poultry rearing introduced which were later applied to game propagation. In particular, incubators and hatchers did away with the necessity of providing and maintaining a legion of broody hens. A machine which can handle 1500 eggs at a time will incubate 3000 in a season when they are set in 500 egg batches. To match this, over 200 broodies would have been needed with each one being fed and watered on a daily basis. To capitalise on this new technology the Eley Game Advisory Service at the ICI Game Research Station (forerunner of The Game Conservancy) started detailed development on the best methods of raising pheasant chicks without their poultry foster parents. This work was greatly helped by the introduction of compound feeds manufactured for the chicken and turkey industries. Keepers could give chicks a crumb food straight from a bag where previously they had relied on all sorts of mashes and preparations including chopped eggs, boiled meat, and large quantities of maggots produced from rotten livestock carcasses. The principal scheme now in use is to transfer newly hatched chicks to brooder units heated by gas or electricity, and as they grow they are allowed access to an outside run. After 6 or 7 weeks the birds are moved to release pens on the shoot where they become familiar with natural conditions, and from where they will be allowed to disperse into the woods and game crops. Artificial feeding is usually maintained throughout the shooting season and often until the following spring to retain birds on the estate. (See Straker & Lealand, 1990, for modern rearing methods). On average 45% of birds released will end up in the bag in the first shooting season after release.

The impact of the new methods on pheasant shooting has been enormous. Pheasant bags are now larger in most districts than pre-war (Figs 8.1 & 8.2). Fig 8.3 shows that the annual bag has increased steadily since the 1950's, as has the number reared and released. However, not all estates keep records of rearing, so although the *trends* are real the actual levels of rearing and bag are not directly comparable in Fig 8.3.

The true relationship between the level of the bag and the number reared is shown in Fig 8.4, which demonstrates that whereas more birds were shot than were released in the 1960's the reverse is now true. However even this includes many wild shoots. For typical reared pheasant shoots the average number released in is well over 350/km². Although the trend in rearing is upwards in all areas, there are regional differences. For example, in East Anglia the bag has not increased with hand-rearing (Fig 8.5), even though in general fewer birds are reared in this region compared to other lowland districts (Fig 8.6). One explanation is that the wild birds are now surviving less well. Like other gamebirds

the diet of the pheasant chick is mainly insects (Hill, 1985), and where insects have been reduced by pesticide use, wild production has probably declined. Fig 8.7 shows the bag from two large Norfolk estates that rely entirely on wild birds; one clearly shows a decline in recent years which is probably typical of most wild shoots, whereas the other appears to have retained the wild productivity.

Hand-rearing can have an indirectly detrimental effect on wild stocks since keepers and owners increasingly manage shoots for released birds and not for the wild ones. For example, temporary game crops provide ideal autumn and winter cover for released birds but these are not suitable for nesting or chick rearing. Also, predator control by keepers is concentrated in the autumn to protect released poults rather than in spring to save nests. However, many permanent pheasant coverts planted primarily for showing released pheasants do also provide good nesting cover around the edge (Gray, 1986) and pheasant breeding densities are high in woodland designed as winter holding cover (Woodburn & Robertson, 1990). More worrying is that reared birds make poor parents in subsequent years, since they are much more prone to predation, parasitism and adverse genetic selection (Robertson & Dowell, 1990). It is probable that pheasant stocks are only maintained at current levels by the constant addition of reared stock and without this the population, and certainly the shooting bag, would collapse (Hill & Robertson, 1988).

Although there may be problems associated with rearing, the creation and management of woodland for pheasants, which rearing encourages, has very significant positive conservation benefits to other species. For example, woodland butterflies are improved in variety and number where woodland is managed for game rather than forestry (Robertson, Woodburn & Hill, 1988).

W. G

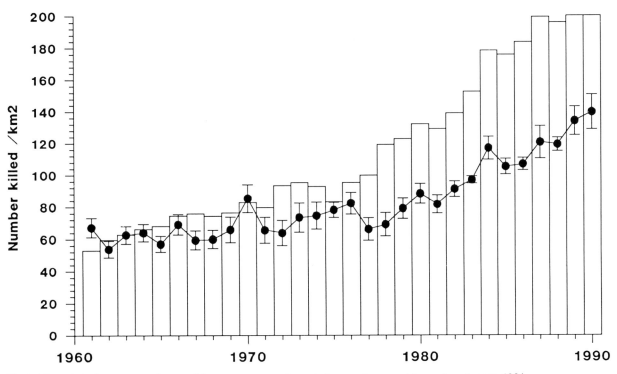

Fig 8.4 Trends in the average bag and the average number of pheasants reared (open bars) since 1961.

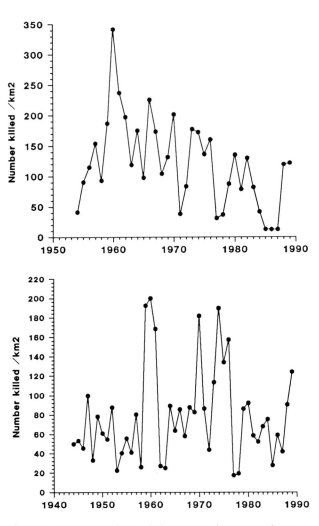

Fig 8.7 Average numbers of pheasants shot on two large estates in Norfolk where pheasants are not hand-reared.

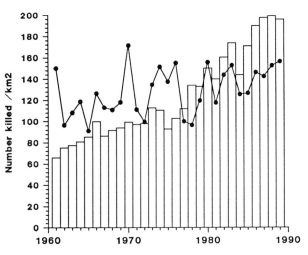

Fig 8.5 Trends in the average bag and the average number of pheasants reared (open bars) since 1961 in East Anglia.

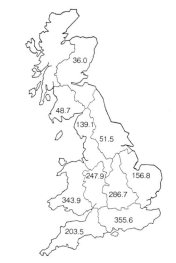

Fig 8.6 Average number of pheasants reared per 100 hectares annually in each region between 1981 and 85. The figure for Wales is based on a small sample, and may be slightly atypical

Red Grouse *(Lagopus lagopus)*

The red grouse, a sub-species of the continental willow grouse, is part of the upland heather moor community. It is regarded by many as the paragon of British game-birds; and its attraction has not yet been superseded by the ubiquitous pheasant. Indeed the cost of a days driven grouse shooting is almost twice that of a pheasant day. Unlike pheasant or partridge shoots, which have been transformed by hand-rearing, grouse shoots are entirely dependant on wild bred birds; partly because reared grouse survive badly when released, but also because the uplands have been much less affected by modern agriculture than the lowlands.

Scotland became a romantic hunting ground for the English after the clearances of the late 18th century, but it was not until the development of the railways in the 1840's that the Highlands were opened up to the fashionable and moneyed southerners. Shooting boxes and hunting lodges were built in profusion by the Victorians and the "Glorious Twelfth" of August, the opening of the grouse shooting season, became a significant and permanent fixture in the social calendar by the 1880's. The shooting practices and moorland management skills developed in those days still remain the backbone of practice today.

The main strategies of keepers managing grouse have always been the twin objectives of controlling pred-ators and burning heather to produce a patchwork of different age growths (Stuart-Wortley, 1894). Heather burning takes place from late winter to early spring, and strips of mature growth 30 to 50 metres wide are fired. Different patches are burnt each year so that a typical rotation might last 12 to 15 years, allowing all grouse access to young pioneer and building heather for food, and longer mature heather for nesting cover. In former days predator control took place on such a wide scale that species like the sea eagle, the hen harrier, the red kite and the osprey were eliminated from all or most of the Scottish Highlands (Newton, 1979). Even

though such predator destruction was regarded by many even then as extreme, the early Parliamentary bird preservation Acts were usually opposed by moor owners. This highly entrenched approach to grouse management was understandable, since the Victorian methods worked exceedingly well and produced large quantities of grouse.

Although red grouse are associated with Scotland, higher bags have always come from the northern English moors (Figs 9.1 & 9.2). Grouse were introduced to Exmoor and Dartmoor in 1915 and small numbers have also been shot there since (Fig 9.2). However, their abundance and range have declined in most areas since the war, due to a continuing loss of heather to forestry, or as a result of intensive sheep management which erodes their habitat (Ball *et al.*, 1982; Hudson, 1986a). These effects are under recorded in our game bag records since for figures like 9.3 and 9.4 we can only include estates which provide continuous records to the present day. These are the estates which have largely resisted the changes. Our figures represent the changes that have taken place on the safeguarded prime areas.

The first serious study of red grouse was the enquiry set up under the chairmanship of Lord Lovat (Lovat, 1911) to try to find a solution to the heavy mortality which occurred on some moors. Their suggested remedy was better burning to improve heather which would produce healthier birds more resistant to disease. It is possible that this policy of better burning yielded some rewards, as the inter-war years were marked by a period of good grouse shooting (Figs 9.3 & 9.4).

During the second war, grouse shooting was largely abandoned as keepers were called up for service and many moors taken over for military training. Thus con-siderable restoration was needed, and a major study was launched in 1956 by the Scottish Landowners Feder-ation as part of an Aberdeen University project, later to be continued by the mountains and moorlands team of the Nature Conservancy and finally as part of the Institute of Terrestrial Ecology. This unique and long-term study, principally conducted by David Jenkins, Adam Watson and Robert Moss, not only produced a wealth data on the biology of grouse but funda-

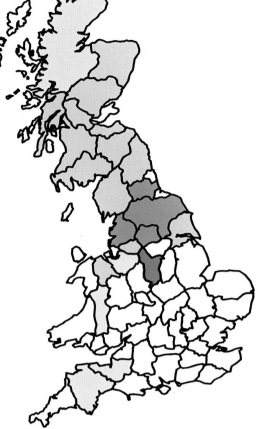

Number of red grouse killed
per km² of grouse moor

> 100

50 - 100

10 - 50

< 10

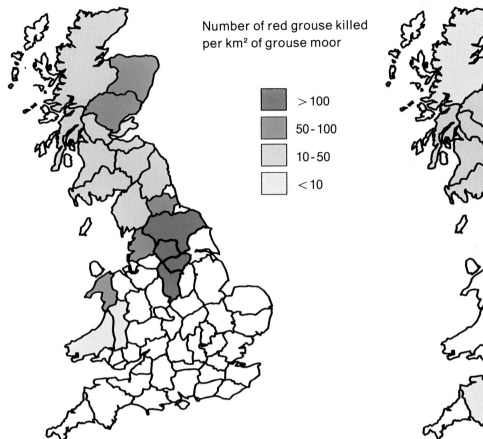

Fig 9.1 Distribution of the average bag of red grouse
between 1900 and 1938.

Fig 9.2 Distribution of the average bag of red grouse
between 1961 and 1985.

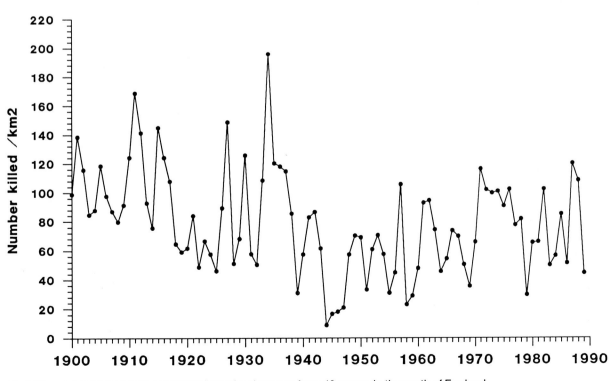

Fig 9.3 Long-term trend in the average bag of red grouse from 13 moors in the north of England.

47

mentally altered biologists' views as to how populations were regulated. The idea that behaviour was a key component in population dynamics was emphasised for the first time and has been a continuing theme throughout their research programme (see Moss & Watson, 1985). The basic idea was that grouse stocks were limited by the number of territorial males in the autumn, and the size of their territories was determined by their aggression and the food supply. Those birds that did not get territories formed part of a surplus that eventually died of disease or predation. These mortality agents were therefore considered simply as final executioners of "doomed grouse" and therefore usually unimportant from the population point of view (Jenkins, Watson & Miller, 1964; Watson & Moss, 1979). It followed from this thinking that disease, particularly Strongylosis, was not a factor regulating numbers and moor-owners should worry more about the condition of the heather than the health of the birds. Even more important, their work implied that predator control by gamekeepers was largely unnecessary and could be dispensed with in most cases. Only where crow populations were very high could some control be justified (Watson & Miller, 1976). Such results made the continuing activities of gamekeepers unpopular with conservationists.

Grouse stocks in England and Scotland significantly improved up to the 1960's (Fig 9.5), but during the mid 1970's, just when Scottish populations in particular should have been reaping the benefits of the new research, there was an unprecedented decline on Scottish moors which continued until the mid 1980's (Barnes, 1987). Concurrent with this decline was a substantial increase in game predators. In particular, foxes (Hewson, 1984), and many raptors (Sharrock, 1976; Lack, 1986) have increased, partly because of diminished control, but also due to increased forestry and rabbit abundance.

Since the late 1970's a Game Conservancy research programme has shed more light on the role of disease in English grouse populations and, recently, the effect of predation in Scotland. This work (funded largely by moor owners under the chairmanships of Earl Peel and Charles Connell) has been carried out by a small unit led by Peter Hudson. This has shown that grouse in Scotland now suffer much higher rates of predation, particularly in winter, than was thought before, and that territorial birds are just as likely to get killed as non-territorial ones (Hudson, 1990). This implies that the idea of a doomed surplus is no longer valid. In fact increased predation is now thought to be the main reason for the Scottish decline (Hudson, 1992).

Grouse shooting bags fluctuate more widely than in most lowland game species, and the long series of records held by many estates provide ample data for analysis (Mackenzie, 1952). Potts, Tapper & Hudson (1984) examined 63 series from English moors and clarified the fluctuations as quasi-cycles (see Appendix II) with an average period of 4.8 years (Fig 9.7). Williams (1985) re-analysed data given by Middleton (1934) and confirmed a 6 year period for these series, but Barnes (1984) looked at 116 moors from Scotland and suggested they had a much wider spread of cycle lengths, and recently Hudson & Dobson (1990) have tied this to regional differences, with cycles getting longer further north (Fig 9.6). There are two contending hypotheses for the cause of these cycles. First, Moss & Watson (1990) believe that changes in behaviour lead to phases of dispersal in grouse populations which cause them to decline. Second, Peter Hudson's group think that periodic outbreaks of the grouse disease Strongylosis are the real cause of cycles (Hudson & Dobson, 1990).

The evidence that disease generates grouse population cycles is now becoming increasingly compelling. First, the life cycle of the disease parasite is sufficiently long that high infection rates picked up during times of grouse abundance can continue to pull the population down over a period of years. Simulation models of this system produce cycles of the required length (Potts, Tapper & Hudson, 1984; Hudson & Dobson, 1990). Second, one finds high levels of the parasitic worm which causes the disease on wet moors where grouse numbers cycle, and only low levels on dry moors which tend not to be cyclic (Hudson & Dobson, 1990). Third, treating parasitised birds to reduce their worm burdens clearly demonstrated that their survival and breeding performance can be increased (Hudson, 1986b). Already some landowners are regularly treating their wild stocks with a medicated grit formula which reduces the parasite. It will be interesting to see whether these moors are consistently able to escape periodic population crashes in future years

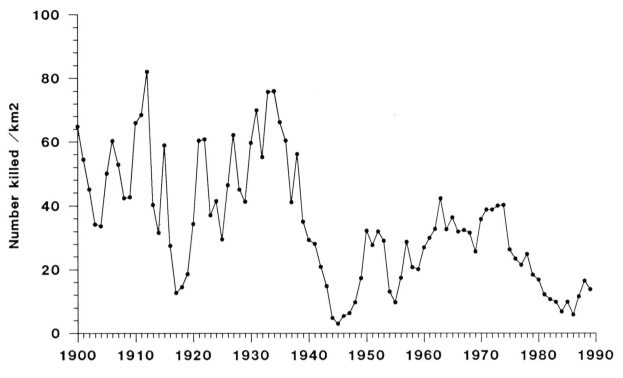

Fig 9.4 Long-term trend in the average bag of red grouse from 44 moors in the Scotland.

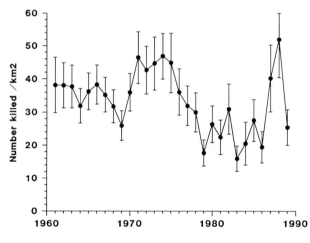

Fig 9.5 Trend in the average bag of red grouse since 1961.

Fig 9.6 Upland areas of Britain which have moors which show different lengths of cycle. Cycle lengths shown in years. From Hudson & Dobson (1990).

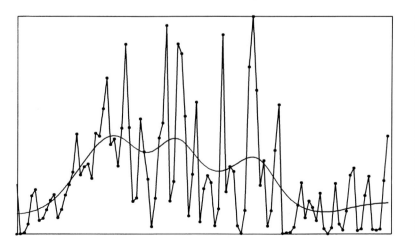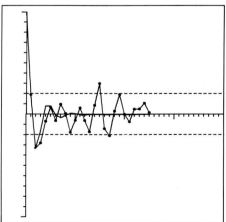

Fig 9.7 Time series and correlogram for red grouse bags from an English Pennine moor. (See Appendix II for technical details).

Black Grouse *(Tetrao tetrix)*

Ecologically the grouse of northern and temperate latitudes can be divided into three groups. The first group are forest birds like the capercaillie and spruce grouse of coniferous zones, and ruffed grouse and hazel grouse of mixed and deciduous woodland. The second group are those of open and scrub habitats, like the red grouse, ptarmigan, sage grouse, sharptail and prairie chicken. The third group is much smaller and consists of one or two species which prefer the transition zone between open ground and forest. In North America the blue grouse of the Rocky Mountains fits in this category, and in Europe the black grouse clearly falls into this same niche—preferring a habitat of open patchy birch and pine woodland interspersed with shrubs and stretches of open ground.

The black grouse is a very selective feeder, choosing the parts of plants rich in protein and switching from trees to shrubs to herbaceous plants depending on what is seasonally available. Thus in Scotland they take nutritious tree buds in spring, move to moorland and boggy areas in summer, feeding on shoots and berries, and finally go back to areas of birch in the late autumn and winter (Baines, 1990). Catkins from birch, young pine shoots, berries from crowberry, bilberry, and cowberry are all useful foods for black grouse. However, cereals are also consumed, and in Scotland, black grouse feeding amongst stubbles and stooks used to be a common sight. Like some other gamebirds the young chicks need insects in their diet for the first two to three weeks of life and hen birds take their broods into rough grass and bog flushes where the chicks can feed on tipulids (leather jackets), caterpillars, and other insects (Kastdalen & Wegge, 1984; Baines, 1990; Niewold, 1990).

In the past black grouse shooting had a distinctive style (Scott, 1937). Being a bird of the moorland fringe, woodland edge and small farm, only a few were shot on the main red grouse drives on the open moor. Also, breeding a month later than red grouse, young birds are not fully grown in August and the best black grouse driving was in October or November, after most red grouse shooting had finished. At this time the black grouse could often be found in large packs feeding in stubble fields along the valley bottoms. These packs flew in and out of feeding areas each day. In such situations large sweeping drives were inappropriate, and shooting parties had to adopt a more flexible approach. When a pack of black grouse was located they positioned themselves in a place where they were able to intercept the birds as they flew off. Beaters were not necessary and only one or two people were needed to disturb the birds to send them winging over the guns in a few moments of intensive action. Marked plumage differences mean it is fairly easy to distinguish the male blackcock from the female greyhen, and even in the excitement of such an occasions, guns were able to select mostly cocks.

Being birds of a marginal habitat one might expect black grouse to have benefited from man's early activities as he broke up the continuous forest, creating clearings for small scale agriculture. Centuries ago this may have happened in Britain as patches of forest were cut down, cultivations started and abandoned, and fire and grazing reduced the original cover. In the more recent past this has happened in Sweden as the boreal forest has been fragmented, and in Denmark where heathlands were intersected by farming (Marcstrom, 1978; Degn, 1978).

This century, however, numbers of black grouse have been declining over most of central Europe including Britain. Indeed the loss of birds in England was taking place even before then, and the decline has involved a loss in range as well as a reduction in density in those areas where black grouse are present. They were formerly common in most of southern England, not only in areas like Dartmoor, Exmoor, and the Quantocks, where they survived until recent years, but also in counties like Hampshire, Dorset, Sussex, Norfolk, and

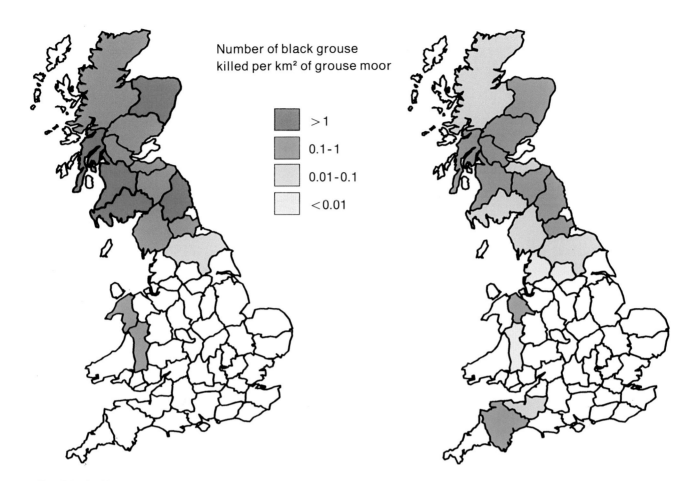

Number of black grouse
killed per km² of grouse moor

> 1
0.1 - 1
0.01 - 0.1
< 0.01

Fig 10.1 Distribution of the average bag of black grouse between 1900 and 1938.

Fig 10.2 Distribution of the average bag of black grouse between 1961 and 1985.

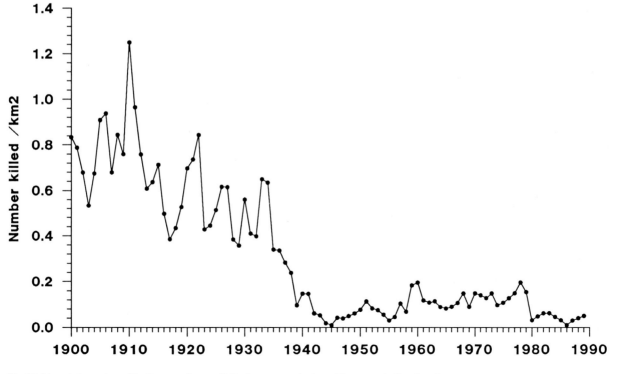

Fig 10.3 Long-term trend in the numbers of black grouse shot on 44 moors in Scotland

Lincolnshire. Indeed Hampshire boasted some quite good black grouse shoots, and Bournemouth town hall now stands on the site of what was one of the best leks. In some places, like the New Forest they were still present until the 1930's, but often only because populations were replenished with released birds. In fact most southern populations were fast disappearing in the late 19th century. Although much of this range reduction occurred decades ago, it is tragically still continuing in recent years. The last wild birds on Exmoor and Dartmoor disappeared in the late 1960's and early 1970's (Picozzi, 1986). Thus although the distribution of the bag before and after the second war shows only a little change (Figs 10.1 & 10.2), the present day distribution is a lot worse than the data would suggest. Even the population in Wales, which seemed to have been increasing in the 1970's, now appears to have declined (Grove et al., 1988) and the number shot in Britain as a whole continued to diminish until the middle of the last decade. Since then there has been a slight recovery, perhaps resulting from new private forestry plantings where the exclusion of grazing animals has temporally increased ground cover and food for black grouse (Fig 10.5).

The reduction in numbers is clearly evident in the long-term series from Scotland (Fig 10.3), showing a noticeable decrease following the first war and complete collapse before the second, after which populations never really recovered. The same pattern of decline is evident from shoots in the north of England (Fig 10.4). In relation to other game species the decline is more severe than either the snipe or the grey partridge. This is curious since one might suspect that greater habitat changes have taken place in the agricultural heartland and home of the grey partridge, than in the uplands of Scotland where this loss of grouse has occurred. This decline is mirrored over much of central and northern Europe. The only places where populations are stable and black grouse still remain common birds are in northern Scandinavia and in parts of Perthshire.

There have been various explanations for the cause of the decline in Britain and elsewhere, and it is impossible to find one hypothesis that fits every case. Historically, overshooting has certainly been advanced as a factor in Scotland (Scott, 1937), but experience in countries like Denmark where the black grouse has been totally protected since 1973 (Strandgaard & Asferg, 1980) shows that declines cannot be prevented simply by stopping shooting. It is probable that several factors are important and a change in any one can send the population towards extinction. There are also some novel explanations, including competition between pheasants and grouse either directly through fighting or indirectly through disease. The main cause seems to rest on the triangle of relationships critical to all game-birds; nesting habitat, food for the chicks, and predation.

Recently David Baines has reviewed the extensive data available throughout Europe on breeding success and he has shown that the number of young reared per hen has gradually been declining, at least since the early 1950's (Baines, 1991). In Scotland in particular, he suggests that the survival of chicks has been reduced, and although the intensification of agriculture and forestry have contributed to this—and poor summer weather may play a part—increased grazing pressure by deer and sheep have been of critical importance.

The existence of cycles in black grouse is not so clearly marked as it is some populations of red grouse. Nevertheless when a number of moors are examined with time series analysis there is evidence of a four or five year quasi-cycle (Fig 10.6) and in some series this is quite marked (Fig 10.7). In Scandinavia, cycles are shorter and probably connected to the distinct cycles that occur in the small mammals which are the main prey for most boreal predators. Indeed, generalist predators, like foxes, switching to birds when small mammals are scarce may be the cause of these black grouse cycles (Angelstam, 1986).

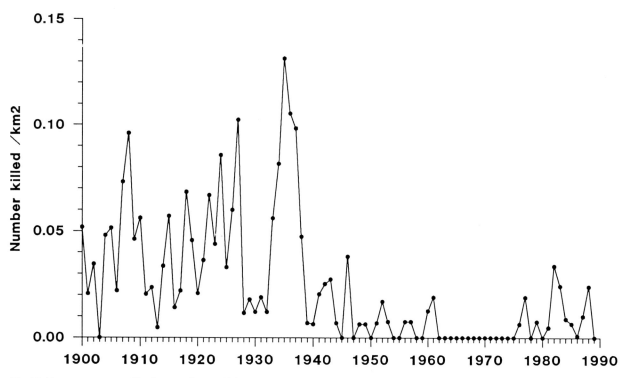

Fig 10.4 Long-term trend in the numbers of black grouse shot on 13 moors in England.

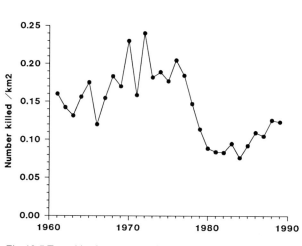

Fig 10.5 Trend in the average bag of black grouse since 1961.

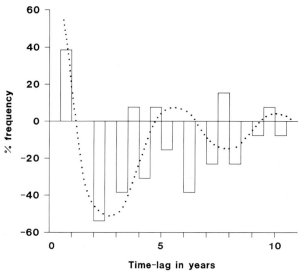

Fig 10.6 Frequency of significant autocorrelations from the analysis of 13 Scottish estates with records of black grouse. (See Appendix II for technical details).

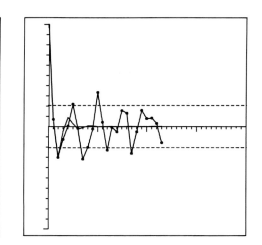

Fig 10.7 Time series analysis of black grouse bags from a Scottish estate. (See Appendix II for technical details).

Capercaillie *(Tetrao urogallus)*

With the final disappearance of the great bustard in the early 19th century, the capercaillie became Britain's largest game-bird. In fact populations of this huge and spectacular grouse also died out in a similar fashion, and our present stock is based on a 19th century re-introduction. The "caper" is a bird of climax boreal coniferous forest and was formerly distributed throughout many of the forests of Scotland and northern England, but relentless deforestation and over-hunting caused a rapid decline to final extinction in about 1770. Paradoxically it was again the sporting interest which encouraged attempts at re-introduction (Lever, 1977). The main success being credited to a Llewellyn Lloyd and Sir Thomas Buxton who put down 45 birds at Taymouth Castle, Lord Beadalbane's Perthshire home, in 1837. By 1862 their numbers were estimated to have increased to between 1000 and 2000 birds. From this beginning, followed by more re-introductions, translocations and natural dispersal, the population spread to most of eastern Scotland by the end of the 19th century and capercaillie shooting became a regular feature on many Scottish estates

Both the recent distribution of the average bag (Fig 11.1) and the trend (Fig. 11.2.) indicate that caper have declined markedly over the last two decades, with the biggest drop occurring since the mid 1970's. Where there are also long-term data (Fig. 11.3), it is evident that the decline goes back over a much longer period, and bags in the 1920's and 30's were much higher than those in the 1960's (Baines, Goddard & Hudson, 1991).

It may seem odd that a forest species should not have benefited from the massive growth in forestry that followed two wars and the establishment of the Forestry Commission. However, the new plantations are quite different from the native Caledonian pine forest they have replaced. Capercaillie like mature or pole-stage coniferous pine woodland with an open structure allowing light to penetrate, giving a rich shrub and herb understory. Modern commercial timber is grown in even aged stands of densely packed trees where little light penetrates and which are clear felled before they become "over-mature". These commercial forests hold fewer caper than native pine woods (Moss, Weir & Jones, 1979), especially if there is no gamekeeper reducing predators. This would be less important if the new plantations were merely supplementing the native forest, but unfortunately this is not the case and old forest has either been cut down or under planted to give way to more profitable stands. Indeed there are few sites where native forest still exists (Fig 11.4) and even these are being regularly damaged (Bain & Bainbridge, 1988).

Apart from their foods, like blaeberry and insects, which are less abundant in commercial forest, capercaillie face problems in adapting to these new habitats. They are birds with a "lek" breeding system in which open clearings in the forest play a vital role. These natural clearings may be rocky outcrops, boggy patches of ground with fallen trees, or even forest roads and rides, which allow males to display to each other from various vantage points. Birds fly into these woodland lekking grounds each spring and males strut up and down logs and stumps, fan their tails, and throw their heads back to make the curious "cork-popping" and creaking noises so characteristic of displaying capercaillie. These leks are traditional sites and act as the hub of several male territories which extend outwards like slices of a cake (Hjorth, 1982). Inadvertent destruction of these lekking grounds by clear felling or disturbance can potentially disrupt breeding over a very wide area.

Finally we must remember that when caper were abundant a hundred years ago, and spreading through the uplands, gamekeeping was at its most intense and there were few or no predators which would have disturbed a hen capercaillie as she incubated her clutch at the base of a pine tree. Now foxes and crows are abundant in most areas, and wildcat and pine marten not infrequent. It is entirely possible that a combination of poorer habitat and increased predation has been responsible for the huge reduction in numbers of this bird which at the moment is perilously close to disappearing altogether from Scotland—for the second time.

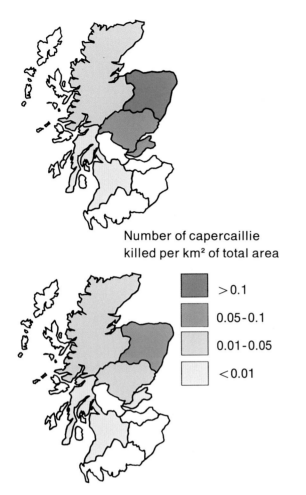

Number of capercaillie
killed per km² of total area

▓▓ (dark)	> 0.1
▒▒ (medium)	0.05 - 0.1
░░ (light)	0.01 - 0.05
□ (white)	< 0.01

Fig 11.1 Distribution of the average bag of capercaillie
between 1900 and 1938 (top); and (below) the distribution
between 1961 and 1985.

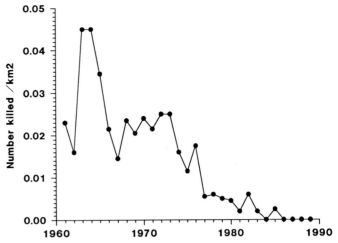

Fig. 11.2 Trend in the average bag of capercaillie since 1961.

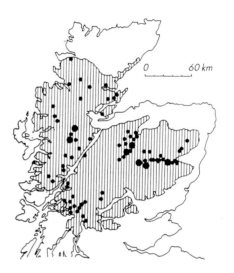

Fig 11.4 Locations of native pine woods in Scotland (black
circles) in relation to the previous extent of original
Caledonian forest. Taken from Bain & Bainbridge (1988).

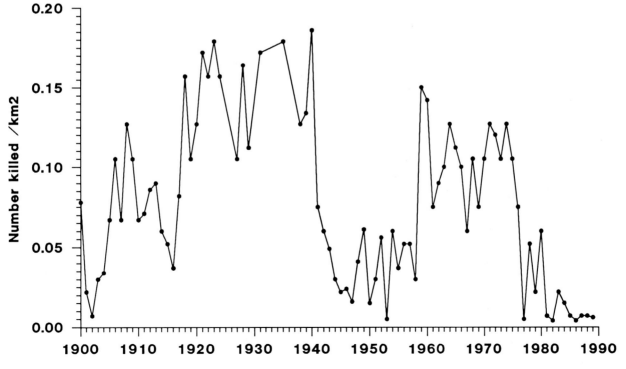

Fig 11.3 Long-term trend from 27 Scottish estates with complete data on numbers of capercaillie shot.

Woodcock *(Scolopax rusticola)*

Although the woodcock is not a primary shooting quarry in Britain it is nevertheless one of the most esteemed of all game taken on shooting days. It has fascinated many sportsmen, not only because it is a challenging and difficult shot, but as a secretive and nocturnal migrant bird its life history still remains somewhat mysterious (McKelvie, 1986). Perhaps because of this woodcock numbers have always been well recorded in game books, and being such a distinctive and recognisable bird there has never been any confusion with other species. However, on the average English mainland shoot the bag is always relatively small and the few that are taken each year can give very little idea of national trends when considered on their own. When combined with results from other shoots, bags do provide a good indicator of the annual and long-term variation in winter numbers.

The breeding range in Britain is thought to have increased in the 19th and early 20th centuries and it now covers most areas except the extreme south west (Sharrock, 1976). The reason for this range expansion is usually ascribed to the creation of shooting coverts for pheasants, which enabled birds to breed in undisturbed open woodland in summer (Shorten, 1974). However breeding numbers may have subsequently declined (Marchant et al., 1990). Until recent Game Conservancy research we knew little of the habitat requirements of breeding woodcock, but now radio-tracking by Graham Hirons (1983) has shown that they are very selective in the types of woods they prefer. Like pheasants, they prefer woods with open areas and skylights, enabling them to fly in and out and allowing males to display (roding) in the air above the canopy, and to see females on the ground. Sufficient ground cover to hide a good nest site is also important. Such conditions are usually a key feature of pheasant coverts. Hirons also found that the species of tree made a difference. Female woodcock raise their brood within the wood, so a woodland floor rich in invertebrates such as earthworms is desirable. Sycamore, ash and alder are species which maintain a good earthworm population in the soil, whereas beech and conifer do not. However woodcock, like other ground nesting game, are very vulnerable to predation (Hirons, 1983), and it may be that their increase was as much due to the removal of predators as to habitat improvement.

It used to be traditional in many European countries to hunt woodcock in the spring. A hunter would quietly position himself at the corner of a wood and wait until evening to shoot roding birds as they flew over the open areas and rides. Such shooting became increasingly unpopular as hunters realised they were shooting the breeding and not the autumn stock. However, detailed research into woodcock breeding biology by Hirons (1983) has shown that such spring shooting may not have been as damaging as it appeared. Unlike many other birds, woodcock do not form monogamous pairs—instead they are polygynous, with some males mating with several females. It appears that roding woodcock are not males defending a territory around a single nesting female, but are competing with one another for air space and flying time above the wood. The best and most dominant males get most air space and therefore display most. Other males get driven off to rode over poorer patches of woodland where there may be no females, and some may even be so low in the hierarchy that they are never allowed to get off the ground. Consequently roding over good habitat is the prerogative of dominant males. A breeding female will entice down one of these males for mating and they then remain together for a one or two days before the male resumes displaying perhaps consorting with another female later. Thus breeding may be accomplished by a very small fraction of the males. Hirons found that if one or more of these dominant males is removed, its place is quickly taken by other subdominants. Thus it is likely that the removal of a few displaying males by hunters will have no effect on the numbers of young produced by the females.

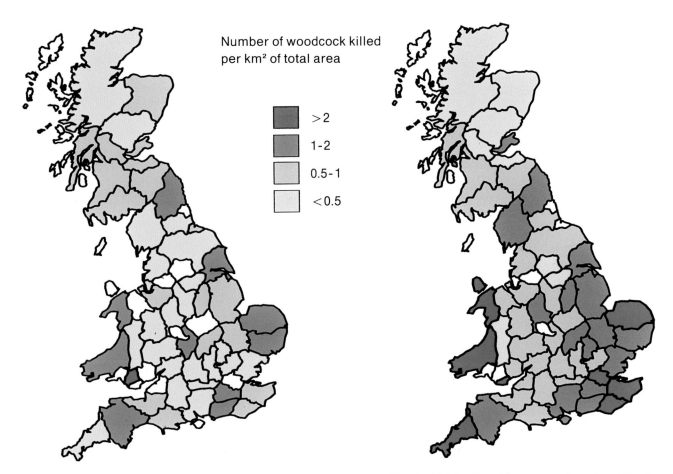

Number of woodcock killed
per km² of total area

> 2
1 - 2
0.5 - 1
< 0.5

Fig 12.1 Distribution of the average bag of woodcock between 1900 and 1938.

Fig 12.2 Distribution of the average bag of woodcock between 1961 and 1985.

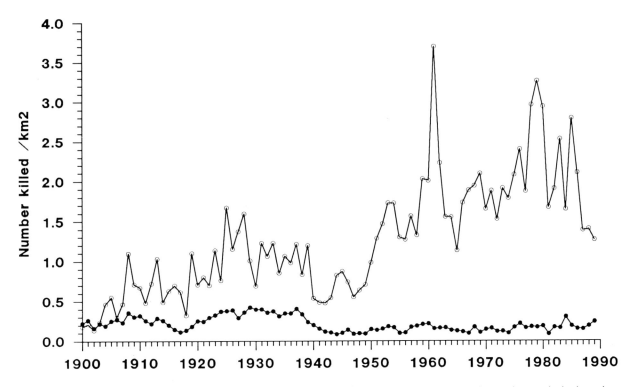

Fig 12.3 Long-term trend in the bag of woodcock from 12 estates in East Anglia and the south east (open circles), and 43 shoots in Scotland (closed circles).

The bag record for south east England since 1961 (Fig 12.2) may support the conclusion that the breeding range has increased, although much of the bag is derived from immigrant birds over-wintering in Britain. Migration of woodcock to Britain occurs in early winter and is most marked during the first full moon in November. Ringing records show that the majority of birds arriving are from Sweden, with rather fewer from Finland and other east European countries (Kalchreuter, 1979). These arrivals, flying generally south west, may remain in eastern coastal counties for a while before moving westwards—many ending up in the western peninsulas. The distribution of the bag shows that the eastern counties along the south west margin of the North Sea have very high woodcock bags, as do the counties of Cornwall, Dyfed and Gwynedd (Figs 12.1 & 12.2).

Most woodcock are taken during normal pheasant shooting days. As beaters drive pheasants out of permanent coverts, so resting woodcock are disturbed and flushed at the same time. However in Cornwall, and one or two other areas where there are high concentrations of over-wintering birds, some specialised woodcock shoots have been developed. Thick coverts of gorse or rhododendron provide holding areas, and these are criss-crossed with rides and tunnels so that dogs can flush birds out of one small patch at a time. The rides also break up the otherwise dense thicket and allow wintering birds to fly in and out of feeding areas at dawn and dusk. Like breeding birds, winter woodcock feed on soil invertebrates, but the winter activity pattern is quite different from summer (Hirons & Bickford-Smith, 1983). A winter day is spent resting and sheltering from the worst of the weather, but the bracken and gorse, which often make ideal cover, provide little in the way of food and at night the birds fly off to open areas to feed. Feeding areas are usually permanent pastures, which contain plenty of earthworms and leather-jackets. This is in sharp contrast to the summer pattern where the woodland itself is also the feeding area.

Wintering woodcock usually remain resident in one locality once they have completed their migration, and some marked birds have been found to return to the same site for several subsequent winters (Wilson, 1983). The best wintering areas are those places where good shelter is close to good feeding. Open bare deciduous woods do not provide good winter shelter, whereas conifers do, so an ideal summer wood will not necessarily be a good winter one. In much of Britain it is probably the scarcity of feeding that limits wintering numbers in some areas. Arable farmland makes unsuitable feeding habitat and only where there is permanent pasture will the soil fauna be rich enough for woodcock.

The bag record shows there to have been a substantial increase in the numbers shot since the war (Figs 12.3 & 12.4). This might be taken to indicate that the numbers of birds over-wintering in Britain is increasing. But since most woodcock are shot on pheasant days, it is more probable that the growth of pheasant rearing has resulted in more pheasant shooting days and so more woodcock being flushed and shot. This argument is supported by the fact that on wild pheasant shoots where the pheasant bag has not increased the woodcock bag has not increased either (Fig 12.5). Furthermore in Denmark, where woodcock are shot on passage from Scandinavia to Britain and other countries (Clausager, 1983), there has been no increase in the bag (Strandgaard & Asferg, 1980). This suggests that the size of the winter migration has not changed. In Scotland where grouse shooting and not pheasant shooting influences the sample, there has been no increase in bag, but of course much of this shooting is done earlier in the season and probably before many of the continental woodcock migrants arrive (Fig 12.3);

There is considerable annual variation in the size of the woodcock bag, and this can be related to the severity of the winter. The colder weather generally leads to a bigger bag and under very severe weather woodcock survival may be much reduced. It may be that the extremely cold winter of 1962/3 not only increased the bag but was also responsible for the rather lower returns for several years afterwards (Fig 12.4). Furthermore, cold weather appears to affect the extent of the winter movement in Britain. Fig 12.6 shows that during a mild winter (1979/80), shoots in central districts shot more woodcock than average, whereas Cornish and other peninsula shoots bagged less. During a hard winter (1978/79) this situation was reversed (see Tapper & Hirons, 1983).

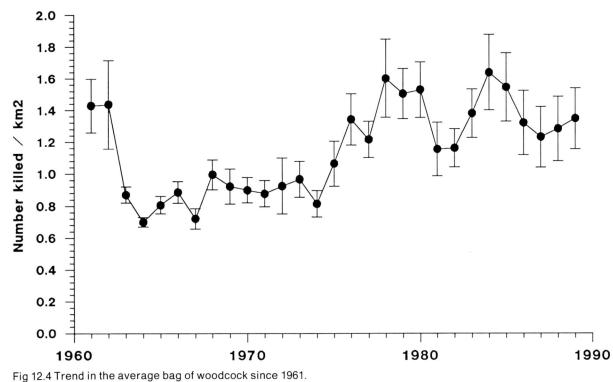

Fig 12.4 Trend in the average bag of woodcock since 1961.

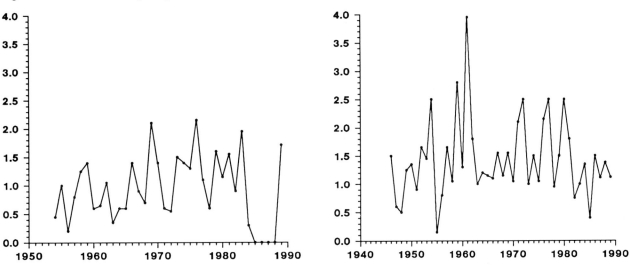

Fig 12.5 Size of the woodcock bag on two large estates in Norfolk and Suffolk where there is no pheasant rearing.

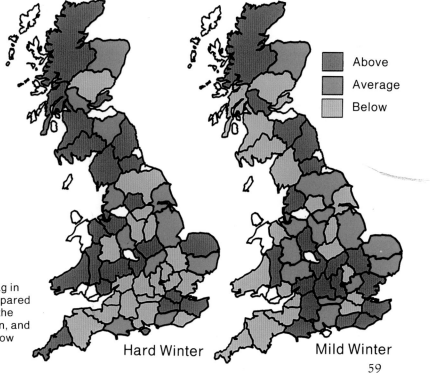

Fig 12.6 (Right) Relative differences in size of the bag in different counties during a hard winter (1978/9) compared to a mild winter (1979/80). Above average is where the county bag is 10% or more above the five year mean, and below average is where the bag is 10% or more below the five year mean.

Above
Average
Below

Hard Winter

Mild Winter

59

Common Snipe *(Gallinago gallinago)*

The snipe has always been a favourite sporting bird and, like the woodcock, it attracts enthusiasts who find a particular magic about shooting a truly wild and unpredictable species, whose occurrence can very often be dependent on the vagaries of the weather and the particular season.

There are actually two species of snipe which occur in Britain during the shooting season. As well as the common species there is the infrequent jack snipe *(Lymnocryptes minimus)*; a smaller dumpier bird with a slightly shorter bill. This species has recently been protected by law (Wildlife and Countryside Act, 1981), though in some instances it may be difficult to tell the two apart whilst shooting. However, the rough shooter should be able to notice the more direct, slower, silent flight of the jack snipe as it flushes away from him, compared to the rising, jinking, noisy flight of the common species (Swan, 1991). In the early years of the National Game Bag Census the two species were separated on the form—though it is doubtful whether all keepers actually made the separation at the end of the day when the bag was tallied. As a result, in a group of west country estates in 1961 only 20 (4%) out of 489 were recorded as jack snipe. However, including only those places where both species were shown, this represented 16% of all snipe. This difference could be due to the fact that jack snipe seem to be a bit more specific about their habitat requirements than common snipe, preferring a slightly wetter environment with more cover—Mike Swan (pers. com.). Harradine (1986) suggests that one in eight (12%) of all snipe shot before the Wildlife and Countryside Act were in fact jack snipe. In our analysis we have excluded any birds recorded as jack snipe.

Like the woodcock, the common snipe breeds in Britain as well as wintering here. But it is not a residential bird, and it migrates between wintering and breeding areas, generally moving south in autumn and north in spring. Thus distribution in Britain tends to be more con-

centrated in Scotland and the north of England in summer and more southerly in winter (see Sharrock, 1976, and Swift, 1986). Also, evidence from ringing shows that many winter birds migrate in from continental populations in Scandinavia and west from Poland and eastern Russia (Cramp & Simmons, 1982). There are also Atlantic populations, such as those breeding in Iceland, which migrate to Ireland, the Hebrides and the Scottish Islands. Some, like Tiree, are particularly noted for their snipe shooting. These migration patterns may be shifting, and particularly the stop-off points for moulting may have changed. Nevertheless, the size of this wintering population is probably huge considering the breeding areas available in Russia and Scandinavia. There may be some 20 to 30 million snipe passing through Europe on Autumn migration and some 1.5 million are taken by hunters (Beintema & Müskens, 1983).

In summer, common snipe choose wet relatively open ground for nesting. Flooded permanent pastures are ideal since they have a wet humus-rich soil which allows snipe to probe for earthworms, leather jackets and other soil insects which are their primary food. Most nest sites are in tussocks of grass, sedge or *Juncus* rushes (Mason & Macdonald, 1976). They are a territorial species with the male doing a characteristic aerial drumming display to attract a mate and keep out rival males. Such displays have frequently been used as an indicator of snipe breeding numbers (Smith, 1983), but since only a small proportion may be displaying at any one time this could considerably under-estimate the breeding density (Green, 1985). Snipe produce a single brood per year, laying a nest of 2 to 5 eggs. However in Britain their breeding success does not appear to be high and in a study of British Trust for Ornithology nest record cards, Mason & Macdonald (1976) found that only 56% of all eggs hatched. Most losses were due to predation (56%) and trampling by livestock (25%). Carrion crows were the main predators but Green, Hawell & Johnson (1987), identified the stoat as a key predator on the

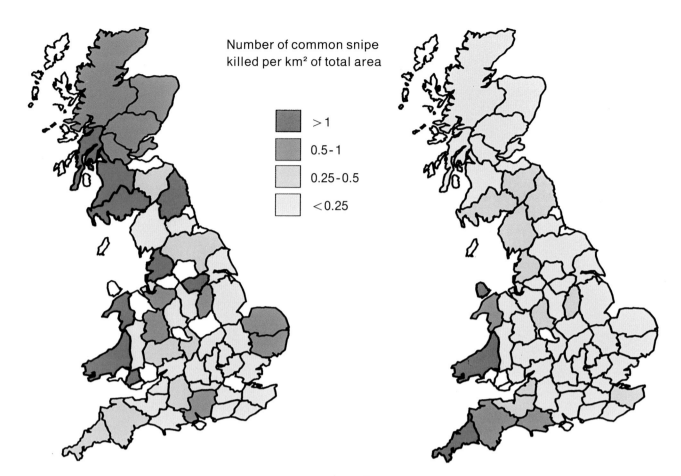

Number of common snipe
killed per km² of total area

> 1
0.5 - 1
0.25 - 0.5
< 0.25

Fig 13.1 Distribution of the average bag of common snipe
between 1900 and 1938

Fig 13.2 Distribution of the average bag of common snipe
between 1961 and 1985

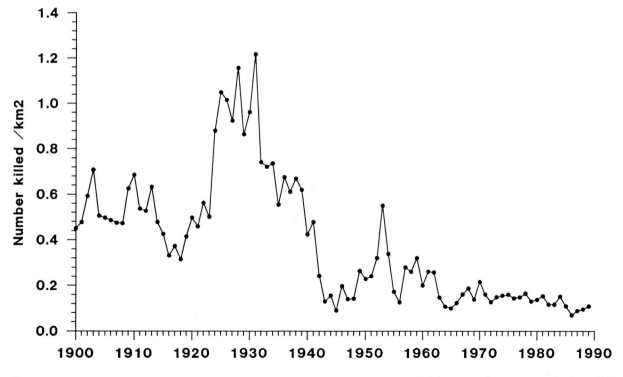

Fig 13.3 Long-term trend in the average bag of common snipe from 72 estates which have continuous records since 1900.

Nene Washes. Mason & Macdonald speculated that this level of loss was too high for the UK population to be self sustaining.

Unlike woodcock, which are commonly shot in woodland pheasant drives, snipe tend to shelter out of the wind on boggy ground amongst tall grasses and sedges. They come out at dusk to open wet patches to feed. Thus only on grouse moors where such boggy areas are taken in during a drive are snipe likely to come over the guns on a shooting day. So if one wants to shoot snipe one must organise the day especially for this purpose. The usual practice is to walk up birds with several guns in a line, however people do organise special drives on areas where the birds are concentrated. Mursell (1981) recounts how this used to be done at Eaton Hall on the Duke of Westminster's estate. In this case special butts were constructed adjacent to the snipe bog for this purpose.

The distribution of the bag pre- and post-war suggests a general reduction, particularly in the north and East Anglia, although the south west appears to be better today than it was pre-war (Figs 13.1 & 13.2). The long-term information (Fig 13.3) shows an even more marked reduction, with modern bags being only about one third of those in earlier days. Although this graph suggests a continuing decline, Fig 13.4 indicates that there has been little real change over the last 30 years. The long-term bag also implies that numbers were increasing during the inter-war years, and Cramp & Simmons (1982) report that snipe abundance around the turn of the century increased following a decline through much of the 19th century. If this information is right, we can trace a decline to about the 1880's, followed by a rise to the second war, then a rapid drop to the lower levels we have today. This long-term pattern is the inverse of profitable farming and the land drainage and cultivation

that went with it. It is interesting that where snipe habitat has been specially retained for shooting, bags have been maintained throughout, implying that winter abundance is now limited by the amount of suitable habitat (Fig 13.5).

In the summer breeding season additional pressures may have come, due not only to the loss of the snipe's preferred nesting habitat (permanent pasture), but also due to higher livestock levels. This would cause increased disturbance and trampling loss during breeding. Fig 13.6 shows how these twin effects could have acted together, squeezing out suitable nesting areas for snipe. Clearly with reduced areas of wetland, habitat conservation is going to be a key factor in retaining reasonable numbers of snipe for shooting in this country. Existing bogs have to be retained, but more importantly we need to encourage the creation of new ones where land is taken out of agriculture, and actively discourage owners from draining their upland moors. Lower stocking rates for sheep and cattle would also help our existing breeding populations.

Finally, we should not forget that for years some landowners have been managing habitat specially for the snipe, and this needs to be encouraged (Harry Wells and Andrew Hoodless pers. com.). For example, moving tethered livestock around a wet pasture will create little feeding circles for snipe, with bits of bare ground fertilised with dung. Cutting out patches of turf in wet pasture also makes it more attractive to the birds. Careful grass cutting can create a diverse pattern of cover and open areas which snipe like winter and summer. With the pressure now moving away from increased farming production, the prospects for improving snipe habitat look considerably better than they did a decade ago.

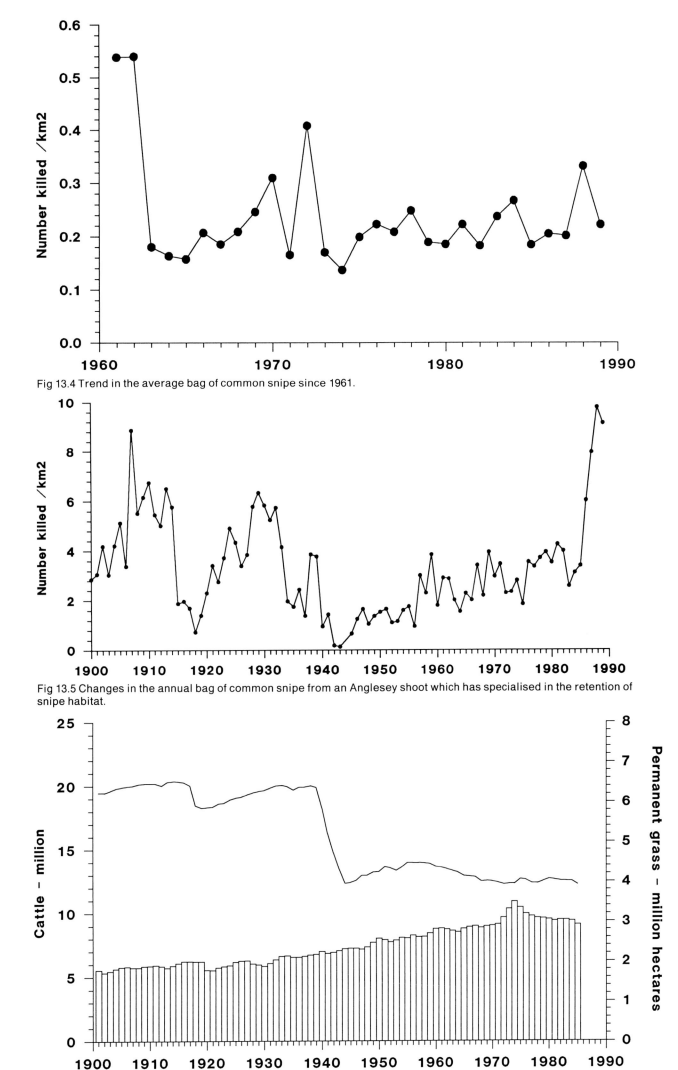

Fig 13.4 Trend in the average bag of common snipe since 1961.

Fig 13.5 Changes in the annual bag of common snipe from an Anglesey shoot which has specialised in the retention of snipe habitat.

Fig 13.6 Changes in the amount of permanent pasture (line) in Britain compared to the total head of cattle (bars). Data from Ministry of Agriculture.

Mallard *(Anas platyrhynchos)*

Unlike many farmland and upland game species which have suffered declines in post-war years following the introduction of intensive agriculture and increased levels of predation, waterfowl populations have generally fared better and most species have remained stable or increased. By far the most numerous and widespread of these is the mallard, although the distribution of the bag (Fig 14.1) not unnaturally shows a heavy emphasis on the lowland shoots of central and southern Britain.

Most duck are shot by taking them at, or near, flight ponds often specially constructed for the purpose. These ponds may be too small to act as resting areas during the day, but are attractive to duck at night if they are fed on a daily basis. Using this technique, duck can be encouraged to flight in regularly each evening to feed, and allowed out again each morning to return to their resting areas. By setting up shooting hides close to where the duck fly in, they can be shot at dusk as they wing their way through the twilight. A properly fed flight pond can be shot at well spaced intervals throughout the winter. Too heavy shooting leads to excessive disturbance and the duck go elsewhere. The construction of flight ponds has been a very popular form of habitat management for waterfowl in recent years (Anon, 1981) and the Game Conservancy's Advisory Service is frequently called upon to plan such features.

Flight ponds often work better with a few decoy birds already on the water, and no doubt this was the initial reason for shooters rearing some tame birds for release as well. However, rearing of duck is now becoming increasingly common, and there has been a steady increase over the last ten years which consequently has increased the bag (Fig 14.2). In most cases only small numbers are reared (less than 500 birds), but occasionally several thousand are produced and duck are shot by driving them off water and shooting them either as they return or fly in to another lake. Much of this increase has taken place in southern districts, whereas in regions like East Anglia the proportion reared and shot has remained relatively constant (Fig 14.3). In spite of this, rearing mallard is not anything like such a common practise as rearing pheasants; for example although some 60% of shoots in the census shot some mallard in 1985, only 14% actually reared any artificially (Fig 14.4) and the total numbers reared regionally are small (Fig 14.5). Thus shooting is still heavily dependant on a flourishing wild population.

Data from wildfowl counts suggest that winter losses are density-dependent and can compensate for current levels of shooting (Hill, 1984). However as natural wetlands have been lost, so it is inevitable that duck populations will increasingly rely on newly created waters such as gravel pits and reservoirs. Restoring these as waterfowl reserves has been a major aim of the joint Game Conservancy and ARC Ltd research on the gravel pits at Great Linford in Buckinghamshire. The first experiments here increased the breeding density by providing better nesting habitats in the form of islands, increased bank length and better bank side vegetation. This work was largely successful, and with predation control, numbers of nesting mallard increased in the reserve site. But, it was apparent that duckling survival was poor, and this was soon attributed to low levels of aquatic insects in the new lakes. Mallard ducklings depend on these insects as a source of protein for growth (Street, 1977), and in the wild, duckling fledging coincides with maximum midge emergence and survival depends on insect abundance (Hill, Wright & Street, 1987). Indeed David Hill found that some of his radio-marked female mallard moved their broods away from the specially made reserve area to the nearby River Ouse to obtain food. Experiments to increase insect numbers using artificial lake substrates such as straw offered a partial and temporary solution (Street, 1983), but it was becoming clear that a major problem was the huge population of fish in the lake which was consuming most of the insect biomass (Giles, Street & Wright, 1990). As a consequence Nick Giles experimentally netted out the fish from the main lake, and has kept them largely fish free since. The result is a substantial increase in insect production as well as a regrowth of aquatic plants which had been absent in the presence of the high fish stock. Now there is a large and more diverse stock of wintering waterfowl because of the better food base, as well as improved mallard and tufted duckling survival (Giles, unpublished).

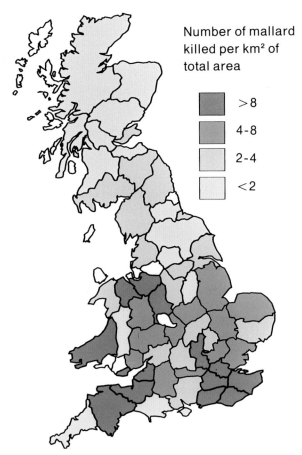

Fig 14.1 Distribution of the average bag of mallard between 1961 and 1985.

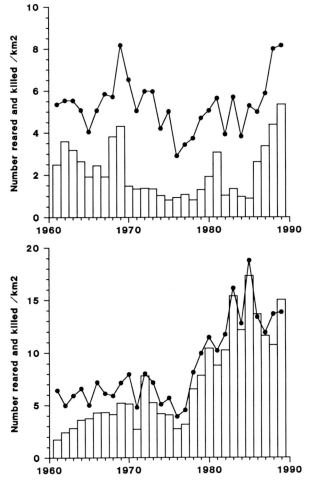

Fig 14.3 Regional trends in numbers of mallard shot and reared since 1961. Above, East Anglia, below the south east.

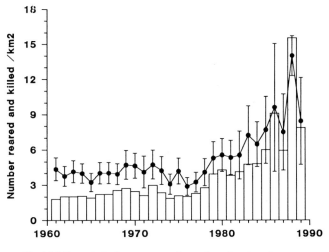

Fig 14.2 Trends in the average bag of mallard and mean number reared and released in Britain since 1961.

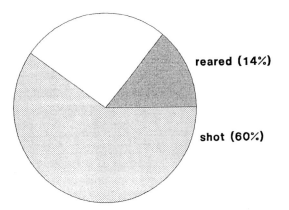
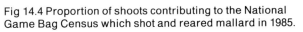

Fig 14.4 Proportion of shoots contributing to the National Game Bag Census which shot and reared mallard in 1985.

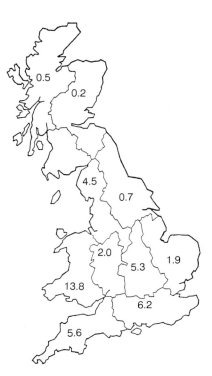

Fig 14.5 Regional differences in the numbers of mallard hand-reared in Britain in 1985. Numbers are per 100 hectares of shoot.

Teal *(Anas crecca)*

A variety of duck are now recorded on the Game Conservancy's National Game Bag Census form, and although probably most are shot by flighting on inland waters, some will also be taken on estuarine and coastal habitats where estates and shoots are by the sea. Although mallard are by far and away the most numerous of the species shot, a diversity of others are recorded (Table 15.1). Of these the most important is clearly the teal.

Teal tend to breed more frequently in the northern and upland parts of Britain where they are a secretive duck, preferring dense cover in marshy or upland bog habitats. They are rather scarce in central and southern England and confined to scattered small local breeding populations (Sharrock, 1976).

In winter however, numbers are considerably swollen by immigrants from Scandinavia, Iceland, northern Russia and the Baltic. Wintering stocks are thus at least ten times those found in summer (Ogilvie, 1986a). These wintering birds drift southwards so that teal distribution in Britain in winter is more southerly than in summer—indeed they are virtually absent from north west Scotland. This distribution is reflected in the bag (Fig 15.1) with southern and coastal counties having generally higher bags than northern and central ones. Fig 15.3 shows the teal bag in relation to two other species, tufted duck and wigeon. The teal features in most regions, whereas the tufted concentrations are on mainly inland water bodies like gravel pits. Wigeon tend to be found less often in the midland areas.

The average numbers of teal shot each winter is shown in Fig 15.2. This indicates no major trend although it does substantiate the suggestion derived from National Winter Wildfowl Counts (Owen, Atkinson-Willes & Salmon, 1986) that there has been a shift upwards in the most recent decade. The wildfowl counts indicate this is an increase from 64,000 to 88,000 birds over the ten years. Certainly the bag shows a similar increase over the same period, but this follows an apparent reduction during the decade before. National wildfowl

counts take place only on the larger stretches of water, where they tend to pick up the large flocks of duck. They are therefore more likely to record a larger proportion of species like tufted duck, than they do others like mallard, which can be found on countless farm ponds and streams and are not accessible for general counting. Teal fall somewhat in between these extremes and Ogilvie (1986a) estimates that the total winter population is probably between 100,000 and 200,000 birds taking into account those that are not counted. However, Harradine (1985) in an analysis of ducks shot by members of the British Association for Shooting and Conservation (BASC) estimated that their bag exceeded 100,000. The total national bag for Britain is quoted at 288,000 (Bertelsen & Simonsen, 1986). Clearly either estimates of the bag are too high or estimates of the wintering birds too low! It is probable that both may be true and indeed Harradine notes that the BASC survey places a rather heavy emphasis on wildfowling as opposed to other forms of shooting. We can use our own bag census data to estimate the national bag in similar way, and since it is derived from a different approach, i.e. numbers of game shot on specific areas of ground rather than by individual hunters, it provides an interesting cross-check on Harradine's (1985) calculation. We can do this by deriving first an estimate of the amount of Britain that is shot over, using Piddington's (1981) survey which gives a total of 12,242,300 hectares (about 30 million acres). Assuming our census data are representative of this shot-over area, we can extrapolate our regional estimates of bag per 100 hectares into a national figure. For 1985 our total of 2459 teal recorded, extrapolates upwards to 60,779. Clearly making such an estimate is fraught with all sorts of assumptions, nevertheless it does support the view that waterfowl bags are substantial compared to wintering stocks. The fact that Harradine's estimate is nearly five times bigger suggests that the true figure may lie somewhere in between. However, we must remember that the statistical errors on all these calculations are likely to be very large and only by considerably increasing the sample size can we improve accuracy.

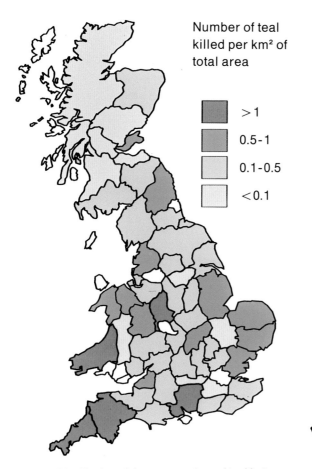

Number of teal killed per km² of total area

▓	>1
▒	0.5-1
░	0.1-0.5
□	<0.1

Fig 15.1 Distribution of the average bag of teal between 1961 and 1985.

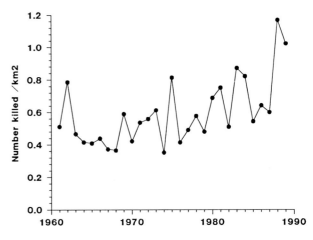

Fig 15.2 Trend in the average bag of teal since 1961.

Table 15.1 Total numbers of duck reported bagged in all areas for the National Game Bag Census, 1985	
Mallard	28278
Teal	2459
Wigeon	399
Tufted duck	334
Pochard	141
Gadwall	122
Shoveler	47
Golden eye	31
Pintail	26

Fig 15.3 Proportions of teal, wigeon and tufted duck in the bag for different regions in 1985. White = teal, Stipple = wigeon, Black = tufted.

Tufted Duck *(Aythya fuligula)*

The tufted duck is one of the few native wild game species which is truly flourishing in modern conditions. It is the only diving duck amongst the small group of inland waterfowl that we regularly record in the National Game Bag Census. It is an open water duck, and so would not normally be encountered on shoots with only small flashes in the form of flight ponds or streams, but where there are lakes or areas of winter flooding, tufted duck are an increasingly common bird. They are mainly diurnal feeders and do not flight in and out to foraging areas like dabbling ducks, so they are not normally bagged with other species at flight ponds. However, when disturbed off a lake they will often fly straight to the next one and it is possible to set up drives for them in this way (Swan, 1991).

Numbers shot have shown a substantial increase since 1961 (Fig 16.2), and this continues a population curve, determined from wildfowl counts, indicating a rising trend since the war (Willes, 1961). This is all the more remarkable since this species was first recorded in Britain as a breeding bird in 1849 (Marchant et al, 1990). Now the population is reckoned to be about 7,000 pairs in summer, with an over-wintering population of perhaps 60,000 resulting from a large influx of birds from Iceland, Scandinavia and northern Russia (Ogilvie, 1986b). Our home reared duck certainly appear to migrate south to France in hard winters but if conditions are not too severe they will remain as winter residents.

Tufted duck, although strictly omnivorous, show a strong preference for animal foods, with molluscs and chironomids being their favourite items. Fledging suc-

cess is dependent on abundant animal foods and experimental trials show that tufted ducklings can quickly seek out and respond to an increased availability of these (Giles, 1989; 1990). It may be no accident that the zebra mussel *(Dreissena)* is a species that is particularly preferred, and this first appeared in the London docks in 1824, spreading rapidly north via the canal system during the early part of the 19th century—at about the same time as the tufted duck were becoming established. This bivalve, which forms large encrustations on under water structures, is an ideal food for tufted duck and in some areas they can feed on them almost exclusively. Although the zebra mussel, combined with an amelioration of the climate, may have been key factors leading to the establishment of the tufted duck in Britain, the activities of man have also benefited them. Today over-wintering tufted are found in concentrations on reservoirs and gravel pits (Owen, Atkinson-Willes & Salmon, 1986), and the post-war creation of these large water bodies, due to a booming aggregates industry (Fig 16.3), is probably the most important factor which has led to their increase. This seems to parallel other species like the great crested grebe, which has benefited too (Prestt & Mills, 1966). The geographical distribution of those shot (Fig 16.1) coincides with the locations of the major gravel workings in recent years (Fig 16.4). Projections of gravel needs suggest a steady growth of excavation over the next two decades. When the economy is growing, the aggregates industry takes in about 15,000 new hectares annually and much of this will later be restored as lakes (Andrews & Kinsmen, 1990).

Most gravel is extracted from shallow fluvio-glacial deposits which are level beds only a meter or two thick and with an over-burden of subsoil of a similar depth. The over-burden and topsoil are removed and pushed to one side before the gravel is extracted and removed for washing. Since most gravel pits are in river valleys, water has to be pumped out continuously during the extraction process. When this process is complete the area can be landscaped using the over-burden to create graded banks and islands before the pumps are turned off, allowing the pits to re-flood (Street, 1983). Gravel pits created in this way provide particularly suitable water bodies for tufted duck since they are generally shallow (usually between 2 and 6 meters) and within the range of the tufted's diving abilities. The techniques of gravel pit restoration for waterfowl have improved considerably during the post-war period and most have been pioneered through a joint venture by ARC Ltd and The Game Conservancy at the gravel workings at Great Linford in Buckinghamshire. This work started by devising habitat creation techniques to improve nesting densities, but later concentrated on methods of increasing aquatic invertebrate production which appears to be the main limit on duckling survival for both mallard and tufted broods.

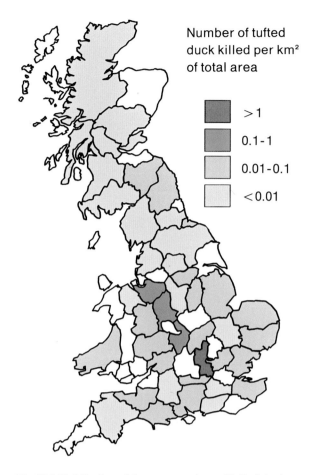

Number of tufted
duck killed per km²
of total area

■	>1
▨	0.1- 1
▨	0.01-0.1
□	<0.01

Fig 16.1 Distribution of the average bag of tufted duck
between 1961 and 1985.

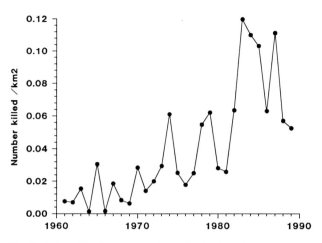

Fig 16.2 Trend in the average bag of tufted duck since
1961

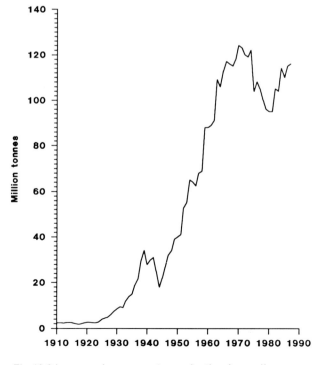

Fig 16.3 Increase in aggregate production from all
sources in the UK. From British Geological Survey (1989).

Fig 16.4 Relative areas of sand and gravel workings that
have been reclaimed for amenity use between 1920 to
1988. Adapted from British Geological Survey (1989).

THE PREDATORS

Hedgehog *(Erinaceus europaeus)*

Studies of the gut contents of hedgehogs killed by gamekeepers show them to be primarily invertebrate feeders. Yalden (1976) found that worms, caterpillars and beetles formed the bulk of their diet, while bird's eggs represented only a small fraction of their food. It is not surprising therefore, that some ecologists have regarded them as harmless to game interests, and consider their control as "probably unwarranted" (Morris, 1977). However, gamekeepers believe them to be significant egg predators, particularly in areas where nests are confined to hedgerows. They also claim that hedgehogs will kill incubating hen partridges and bantams, and surprisingly they have even reported seeing hedgehogs killing significant numbers of pheasant poults in a release pen. Studies of nesting partridges on areas where other predators, such as crows and foxes are scarce, support the view that they are important nest predators (Tapper, Green & Rands, 1982). In spite of the fact that hedgehogs are now partially protected by the Wildlife and Countryside Act (1981), they continue to be killed unintentionally in tunnel traps set for stoats and rats. In some places in Norfolk it used to be customary in summer to use a dog to hunt and kill hedgehogs in hedgerows.

Although most hedgehogs interrupt hibernation to move at least once during winter (Morris, 1973), much of the time they are confined to their nests until April. Continuous trapping records reflect this, showing very few killed over winter, a very large peak in April/May when they emerge from hibernation to breed, followed by a diminishing number taken throughout the summer until November, when the last of the year's young go into hibernation (Fig 17.3).

Hedgehogs appear to be much more patchily distributed than either weasels or stoats, and Fig 17.1 supports the Biological Records Centre distribution map for this species, which suggests they may be absent from many upland areas, particularly in Scotland

(Arnold, 1984). But even in the south of England some estates in Hampshire and Wiltshire kill many more, in proportion to other ground predators, than estates in other districts. This can be illustrated in Fig 17.4 which shows the frequency distribution of the average hedgehog kill per county compared to weasels and stoats. The hedgehog data show a greater number of counties in the less than 1 per 100 hectares category than either weasels or stoats, yet they also show more counties in the 4 to 5 and 5 to 6 categories. This indicates that hedgehogs are more aggregated regionally than either of the other two species killed by the same methods. Hedgehogs probably do best in counties where woods and dense hedgerows offer good cover for their winter and summer nests (Morris, 1973; Reeve & Morris, 1985), and where open pasture provides good foraging areas for their invertebrate food. Fig 17.1 probably reflects this as well as the degree of interest by the landowner in gamebird management.

In some years hedgehogs may be exceptionally abundant (Fig 17.5), and this may result from successful second litters by a significant proportion of the population (Jefferies & Pendlebury, 1968). However, nationally Fig 17.1 suggests a steady reduction in numbers being killed, and the older records indicate that this reduction may have begun prior to 1961 (Fig 17.5). The reason for this is far from clear. It may reflect an actual reduction in population—perhaps due to an increase in tillage as a consequence of simpler cereal growing rotations or a loss of hedgerow cover. Alternatively, it may result from less effort being made by gamekeepers to control small ground predators in general, due to the increasing trend towards hand-rearing gamebirds. The latter seems most likely, as some estates with no rearing show little change in the numbers of hedgehogs being killed. Also, since the Wildlife and Countryside Act (1981) some estates no longer report the numbers of hedgehogs killed.

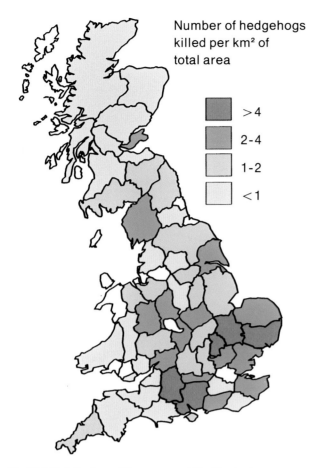

Number of hedgehogs
killed per km² of
total area

> 4

2-4

1-2

< 1

Fig 17.1 Distribution of the average kill of hedgehogs
between 1961 and 1985.

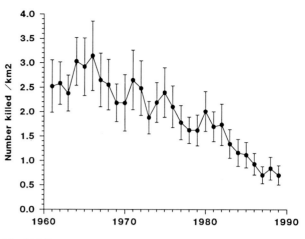

Fig 17.2 Trend in the average kill of hedgehogs since
1961.

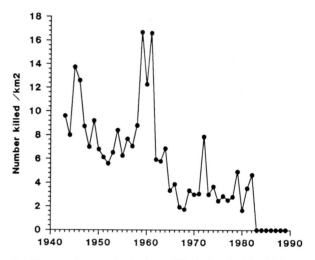

Fig 17.5 Numbers of hedgehogs killed on a Hertfordshire
shoot since 1942.

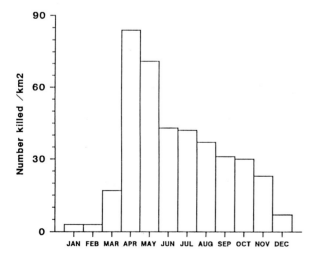

Fig 17.3 Total numbers of hedgehogs killed in tunnel traps
over a nine year period on a Sussex downland shoot in
the 1960's

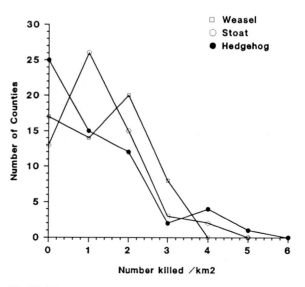

☐ Weasel
○ Stoat
● Hedgehog

Fig 17.4 Frequency distributions for the densities of
hedgehogs, weasels and stoats killed per county in
Britain from 1961 to 1985.

Weasel *(Mustela nivalis)*

The weasel's importance as a game predator is somewhat debatable, even though there is clear evidence that they do kill some partridge chicks (Tapper, 1976). However, they are known to have a big impact on some songbirds, and weasel predation was a most significant form of chick mortality in the long-term study of great tits in Wytham woods, Oxfordshire (Dunn, 1977). From the keeper's point of view, there are sufficient stories of weasels killing chicks, often on rearing fields, for them to feel justified in trapping them.

Almost all the weasels killed by gamekeepers will have been killed in tunnel traps, and very few are likely to have been shot. Females (60 grams) are smaller than males (120 grams) and are less frequently caught (King, 1975a). Perhaps lighter females may be less likely to spring a trap, or the males, ranging more widely, have a greater probability of capture (King, 1975b). There are two seasonal peaks in capture each year; March/April, and August/September (Fig 18.3) The early peak coincides with the break up of over-winter territories and the beginning of breeding, when males are very mobile (Erlinge, 1974); the second peak includes the young of year.

There are marked annual differences in production of young associated with changing abundance of food. On open farmland weasels prey mainly on field voles (Moors, 1975; Tapper, 1979) and when their numbers crash, the weasels fail to breed (Tapper, 1979). Weasel numbers may follow field vole numbers, which are quasi-cyclic, peaking in abundance every 3 to 4 years. The number of weasels captured in the autumn is correlated with the number killed the following spring;

thus yearly totals provided by gamekeepers probably smooth out real changes in density, since they represent the production of two breeding seasons. Some gamekeepers' records show cyclic fluctuations in numbers (Fig 18.4) and time-series analysis confirms a 3 to 4 year quasi-cycle. However, not all series are cyclic and this may be because in habitats such as woodland, weasels feed on other rodents such as bank voles which are less cyclic than field voles (King, 1980a).

The national trend indicates a progressive decline in the number of weasels killed since 1961 (Fig 18.2). This is most marked in East Anglia and the east Midlands, but in the south-west and Scotland it is barely noticeable. There appear to be two main reasons for this reduction;

(1) There was a significant increase in weasel abundance following myxomatosis in rabbits (Jefferies & Pendlebury, 1968; King, 1980b)—Fig 18.4. This arose from an increase in field voles, because grassland (previously grazed down by rabbits) grew into suitable vole habitat. The recovery of rabbit populations has reversed this.

(2) The increasing reliance on hand-reared game means that tunnel trapping is concentrated into a spring offensive rather than maintained all year, so trapping now catches the spring peaks while the autumn peaks are no longer recorded.

The map (Fig 18.1) shows most weasels are killed in arable farming counties where a wild game interest is high and where livestock do not graze out grassy hedgerows and banks.

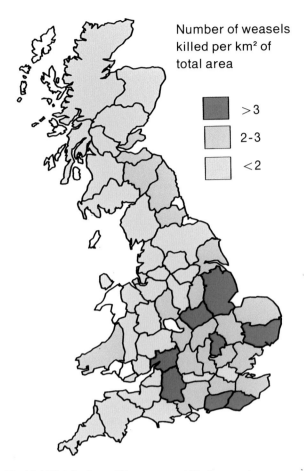

Number of weasels
killed per km² of
total area

■	> 3
▨	2 - 3
▫	< 2

Fig 18.1 Distribution of the average kill of weasels between 1961 and 1985.

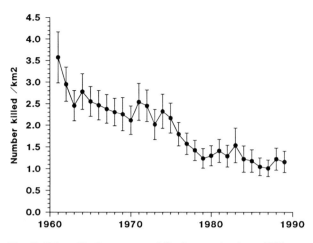

Fig 18.2 Trend in the average kill of weasels since 1961.

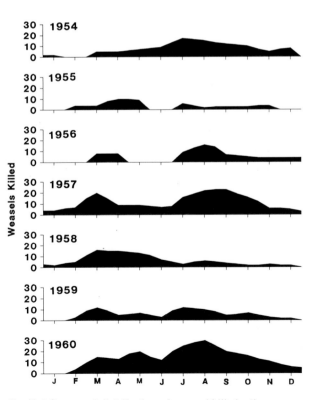

Fig 18.3 Seasonal distribution of weasel kills by three keepers using tunnel traps on a Sussex shoot

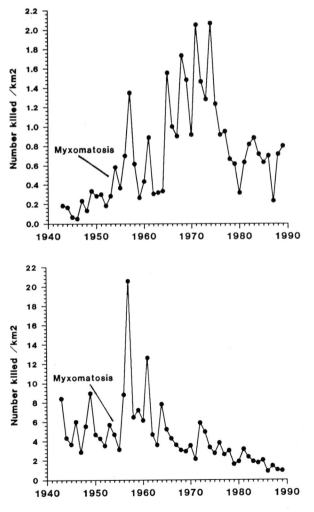

Fig 18.4 Changes in numbers of weasels killed on two estates since 1943, showing the increase following myxomatosis (1956-74 top; 1956-61 bottom), and the tendency to cycle every 3 to 4 years (top).

Stoat *(Mustela erminea)*

Stoats are not large predators (males weigh 320 grams; females weigh 215 grams), but they are capable of killing game animals several times larger than themselves (Hewson & Healing, 1971). Often hen gamebirds are killed whilst incubating, and gamekeepers have observed stoats roll eggs away from partridge and pheasant nests. They will also take growing chicks (Tapper, 1976), and indulge in surplus killing if they get into rearing pens (Hewson & Healing, 1971). Keepers therefore rightly regard them as important game predators and tunnel trapping is designed to eliminate them from the wild game-bird beat during the nesting season—which in many cases it does (Tapper, Green & Rands, 1982). Most of those recorded by keepers will have been taken in tunnel traps, although a significant number are also shot after being "squeaked up" by the keeper mimicking an injured rabbit sound.

Stoats are more generalist predators than weasels (Erlinge, 1983; King & Moors, 1979), but in lowland Britain they have again become largely dependent on rabbits as a primary food (Day, 1968; Tapper, 1976). Their social organisation may in part be a reflection of food supply (Erlinge & Sandell, 1986) but normally the population will consist of resident territorial males, territorial females, and transient males. In spring and summer this territorial structure breaks down as males compete for old and young females as mates (Erlinge & Sandell, 1986). There then follows a long pregnancy,

with delayed implantation, so the young are not born until the following April (Deanesly, 1943), by which time the females will have settled in the territory of another male. Females will often disperse with their families in mid-July and some gamekeepers' records show a distinct peak in captures in this month (Turner, 1954). However, others also show a spring peak in captures, similar to weasels.

Stoats are trapped throughout Britain and there is no large variation in the county distribution (Fig 19.1), although East Anglia and some southern counties have slightly higher totals than counties with a large proportion of upland grouse moor. However, the stoat's fortunes seem to be very much tied to the rabbit's, and myxomatosis has had a profound effect on the species. Fig 19.3 shows the number of rabbits and stoats killed on a Suffolk estate since the war. It shows a more than tenfold reduction in stoats killed after myxomatosis, as well as a recovery as rabbits increased again until 1976. Such changes underlie the increase shown in the national trend to 1975 (Fig 19.2), but not all regions have had similar rates of increase and northern districts show little change compared to southern and eastern areas (Fig 19.4). This is associated with the rate of increase in rabbits which appears to have been less in northern areas (see the Rabbit p 25; Trout, Tapper & Harradine, 1986).

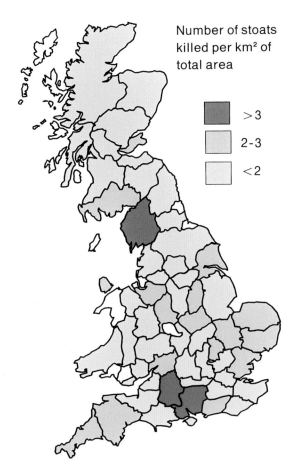

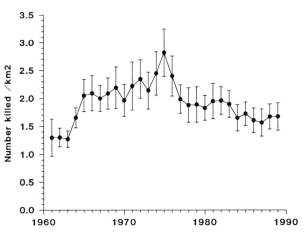

Fig 19.2 Trend in the average kill of stoats since 1961.

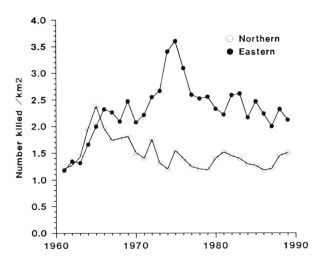

○ Northern
● Eastern

Fig 19.4 Trend in the average kill from northern districts compared to south eastern districts .

Number of stoats
killed per km² of
total area

▣ >3
▨ 2-3
□ <2

Fig 19.1 Distribution of the average kill of stoats between 1961 and 1985.

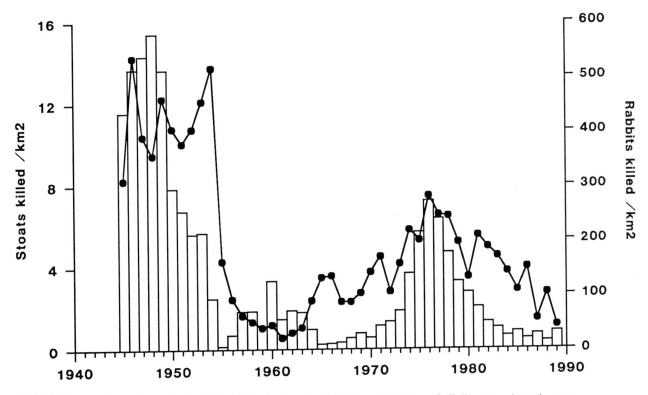

Fig 19.3 Changes in numbers of stoats (line & circles) and rabbits (bars) killed on a Suffolk estate since the war.

Polecat *(Mustela putorius)*

Although this carnivore is currently restricted in range to Wales and the west midland counties, it was formerly widespread and abundant throughout England, Scotland and Wales. It's decline during the 18th and 19th centuries coincided with the development of driven game shooting and the sporting estate. There seems little doubt that trapping and shooting by gamekeepers were largely responsible for this reduction in range, as they were for other predatory mammals and birds (Langley & Yalden, 1977), although polecats were also clearly regarded as pests by most country people who kept poultry. At their minimum, at the start of the first war, polecats were probably only common within an area of forty miles (64 kilometers) radius around Aberystwyth. Since this time, and especially since the 1950's, they have gradually been regaining some of their former range (Walton, 1964; 1968). This contrasts with the situation in Denmark, where polecats have been in decline since the mid 1950's in spite of a reduction in hunting and trapping (Jensen & Jensen, 1972).

The polecat is a generalist predator, taking a wide range of vertebrate prey. It is often associated with lowland and aquatic habitats (Walton, 1977), and it's attraction to farm buildings and poultry houses undoubtedly bring it into conflict with gamekeepers, especially around pheasant rearing or release pens.

There are three particular problems associated with the interpretation of the bag record of polecats: (1) The animal's restricted range, with correspondingly few census contributors from Wales, means that our data are sparse; (2) Polecats were not specifically listed on the National Game Bag Census record form until 1977; (3) It is difficult to distinguish some escaped ferrets from wild polecats, and although contributors are warned against misidentification, some confusion probably does arise.

Taking the above into account, Fig 20.2 indicates that the bag has been increasing since the late 1960's, and this was noticeable even before 1977 when the species was added to the form. Although this trend is clearly significant, the small sample and large variation means that confidence intervals are very wide and the annual differences may be spurious. While this increase does result from a larger number of polecats being killed in some places where they have been consistently reported, the inclusion of polecats on the recording form has increased the proportion of estates listing them with other predators (Fig 20.3). Schedule 6 of the Wildlife and Countryside Act (1981) prohibits the use of spring traps and certain other methods for killing polecats, but otherwise keepers can still take them if they need to.

These data, together with reports from estates in the west midlands, suggest that the species is increasing in abundance and continuing to spread.

For secretive nocturnal species like the polecat, it is very likely that gamekeepers will be the first to record their presence in a new area. Fig 20.4 shows the location of estates which recorded polecats between 1981 and 1985. Clearly, if these are indeed wild polecats and not escaped ferrets, then the species has pushed well beyond the range suggested by the current Biological Records Centre map. Nevertheless, within this range polecats are almost certainly more numerous in Wales than in the west midlands. This is in part suggested by the distribution of the bag (Fig 20.1), but particularly by the numbers killed per estate in the two areas (Fig 20.5).

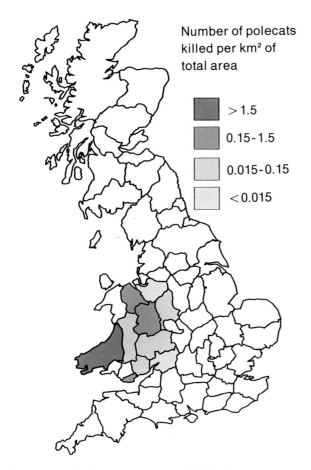

Fig 20.1 Distribution of the average kill of polecats between 1961 and 1985.

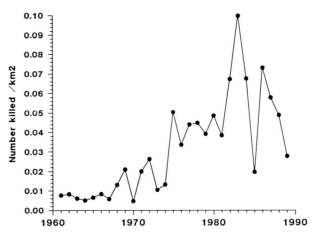

Fig 20.2 Trend in the numbers of polecats killed since 1961 in Wales and the west midlands.

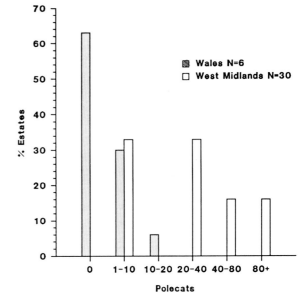

Fig 20.4 Locations of estates which recorded polecats between 1981 and 1985 (black circles), compared to range evident from Biological Records Centre (light stipple; from Arnold, 1984), and the animals minimum range in 1915 (dark stipple; from Langley & Yalden, 1977).

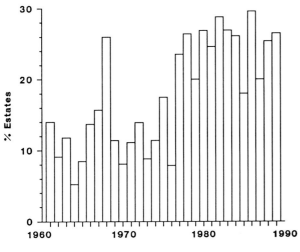

Fig 20.3 Proportion of estates in Wales and west midlands which recorded polecats on their list of predators since 1961.

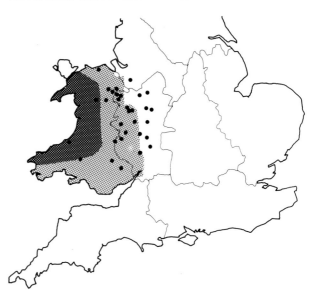
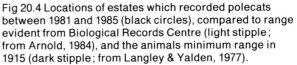

Fig 20.5 Percentage frequency distribution of estates recording different numbers of polecats killed in 1983.

American Mink *(Mustela vison)*

The mink found in Britain is the North American, not the European species *(Mustela lutreola)* which has never been present in this country. The two are close relatives, and it is thought that their common ancestors spread from America across the Bering land bridge to Asia and Europe during the Pleistocene. The range of European mink has now been reduced to north west France and eastern Europe and is contracting, often simultaneously with the spread of the North American animal. The spread of American mink in Britain results from the numbers of animals which have escaped from fur farms since 1929. Only a few got loose from the early farms and there were never enough to establish feral populations. However, after the war mink farming increased, and by the early 1960's it was producing over 200,000 pelts per year with the inevitable escapes, as well as some intentional releases (Thompson, 1964). This enabled wild breeding populations to become established, and the first records of wild bred young were from Devon in 1956. In 1961 mink were discovered breeding on the Hampshire Avon, and at about the same time in south west Wales (Thompson, 1964). Soon afterwards other pockets were found in Sussex, Lancashire, West Yorkshire (Clark, 1970), and in Scotland (Cuthbert, 1973).

Early reports in the National Game Bag Census of mink being killed by gamekeepers were fragmentary, with only 126 being recorded in the first five years (1961-65). Although some were undoubtedly escapes, their distribution (Fig 21.3) indicates they were largely from the then known established populations. The increase in mink numbers since the fifties is well known and has been to a large extent documented through the increasingly desperate attempts by the Ministry of Agriculture to contain their spread. During the five years (1981-85) over 3900 mink were recorded killed by keepers in the

census and the species range has clearly expanded. Only in East Anglia and East Yorkshire do numbers appear to be low. The distribution map (Fig 21.1) closely corresponds to the Biological Records Centre map (apart from Wales, where we are short of contributors)—Arnold (1984), and suggests that mink are most numerous in the Devon, Cornwall, East Sussex, and southern Scotland. However, in eastern and central England data from a recent otter survey suggests that mink are becoming established in these areas too (Strachan *et al.*, 1990).

The rate of increase in numbers suggests rapid growth (Fig 21.2), with the rate being higher in the southern counties. Reports from eastern England are now also beginning to show a clear increase (Fig 21.5).

However unfortunate it may be, it must be recognised that this animal is firmly established over the greater part of Britain and there is no possibility of eradication. A large mustelid of this kind inevitably comes into conflict with game and fishery interests. In the past, escaped animals were often reported raiding poultry houses and killing other small domestic stock. This to some extent still continues today, and a mink getting into a release pen or ornamental waterfowl collection can wreak havoc. However, their diet in the wild appears to be mainly fish, with water birds and mammals as alternative prey (Akande, 1972; Chanin & Linn, 1980); and it is on populations of these animals that mink may have had their biggest impact. Moorhen numbers have shown a significant decline in the British Trust for Ornithology's Waterways Bird Survey (Carter, 1991), and the circumstantial evidence suggests that the water vole has suffered in a similar way (Jefferies, Morris & Mulleneux, 1989).

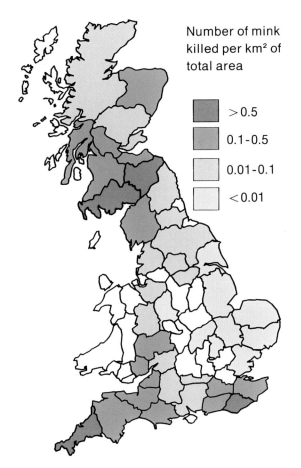

Fig 21.1 Distribution map of the average kill of mink between 1961 and 1985.

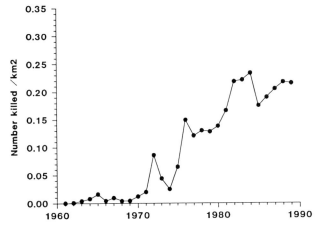

Fig 21.2 Trend in the number of mink killed in Britain since 1961.

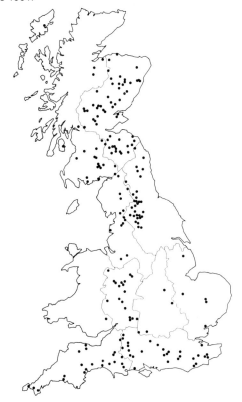

Fig 21.4 Localities of estates that recorded mink killed between 1981 and 1985.

Fig 21.3 Localities of estates that recorded mink killed between 1961 and 1965.

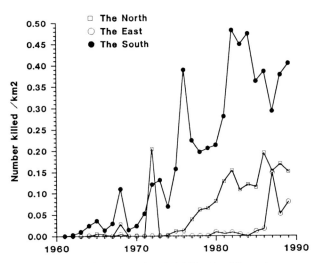

□ The North
○ The East
● The South

Fig 21.5 Rates of increase in mink killed in different regions.

Wildcat *(Felis sylvestris)*

The native wildcat is now restricted in range to upland areas of Scotland north of the central lowlands. However, its range probably covered most of Britain in early mediaeval times. But unlike the polecat, which remained established throughout England and Wales until the early 19th century, the wildcat's range had already contracted to the uplands of Wales, the north of England and Scotland by this time. This was long before the development of the gin trap and the introduction of game preservation. It is therefore likely that deforestation was the initial cause. Extensive trapping for game preservation, particularly on upland moors, where the species had held out temporarily, was responsible only for the wildcat's final clearance from all areas of Britain except the north-west Highlands of Scotland (Langley & Yalden, 1977).

Since this decline, wildcats have increased their range in Scotland. Two world wars and the consequent reduction in gamekeeping, as well as increased forest planting, have allowed the wildcats to expand their territory. Taylor (1946), in a survey of Forestry Commission lands, showed them to be re-established east of the Great Glen—indeed occupying most of their present day range. Jenkins (1962) sent questionnaires to many Scottish estates; their replies indicated that wildcats appeared to be increasing in abundance. Since the sixties, evidence for further range extension is equivocal, and there is very little difference between the Biological Records Centre maps published in 1978 and 1984 (Arnold, 1978 & 1984).

Gamekeepers' records provide evidence of both distribution and abundance of wildcats (Fig 22.1) and indicate they are more common in the north-west. Fig 22.3 shows the distribution of estates which recorded wildcats killed in 1984. Most records are within the area given by Arnold (1984) but a few points suggest the true range may include Caithness and southern Perthshire. This may not represent a range extension but rather inadequate recording of a secretive species. The problem is compounded by the presence of feral domestic cats and domestic/wild hybrids. Seventy percent of estates which killed wildcats also killed feral cats.

Fig 22.2 suggests that the number of wildcats killed increased at least until the late 1970's, and this may have reflected an increasing population. However, two factors have affected this series and must be taken into account: (1) Wildcats were not listed on the National Game Bag Census record form until 1977, and (2) a large proportion of the data were collected in Richard Barnes' survey (see Appendix I) which was retrospective. This means our sample size has increased substantially since the mid 1970's (Fig 22.4). The first factor could cause a difference before and after 1977, while the second factor should increase the reliability of the data. However, Fig 22.4 also shows that the proportion of estates recording wildcats has gradually increased, so the trend is not just the result the chance inclusion of a few more places which take a large number of wildcats. This, and the fact that some individual estates record wildcats with increasing frequency (Fig 22.5), does suggest that the species has became more common over the last twenty-five years.

The Wildlife and Countryside Act (1981) gave partial protection to wildcats, outlawing certain forms of trapping but allowing keepers to continue to shoot them to prevent damage. This appears not to have affected the numbers being recorded. However in 1988 the species was moved on to Schedule 5 of the Act, giving it total protection. As a result the species no longer appears on our data form. The justification for this additional protection (Easterbee, Hepburn, & Jefferies, 1991) is based on a survey which suggests that although the species has spread into most suitable habitats north of the central lowlands since the war, it still suffers from local extinctions and decreases. Furthermore, some of these decreases have been in the relict population that survived in the north-west highlands where there was little hybridisation with domestic cats, making these populations a particularly valuable genetic stock.

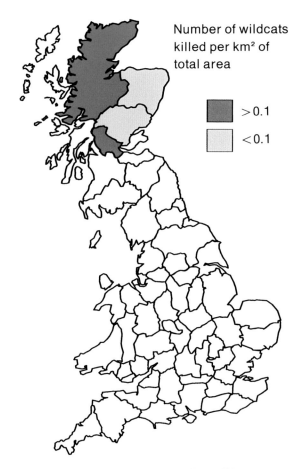

Fig 22.1 Distribution of the average kill of wildcats between 1961 and 1985.

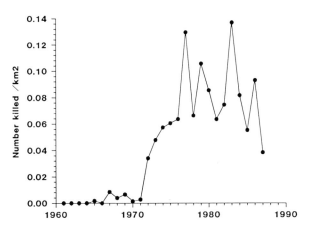

Fig 22.2 Trend in number of wildcats killed in Scotland since 1961.

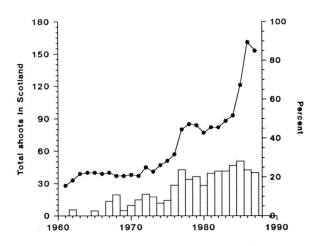

Fig 22.4 Total number estates contributing predator records in Scotland (black circles) and the percentage of these that have recorded wildcats each year (bars).

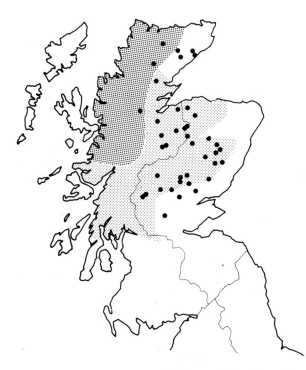

Fig 22.3 Locations of estates which recorded wildcats in 1984 (black circles) compared to the range evident from the Biological Records Centre (light stipple, from Arnold, 1984), and the animals minimum range in 1915 (dark stipple, from Langley & Yalden, 1977).

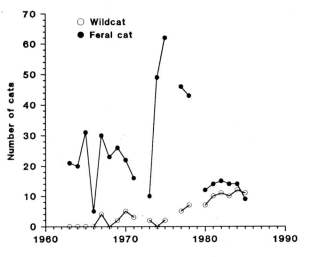

Fig 22.5 Total numbers of wildcats and feral cats killed each year on a Perthshire estate.

Red Fox *(Vulpes vulpes)*

The fox is widely regarded as the most serious of all mammalian predators, since it is very numerous and will take game at all seasons and in most habitats. However, summer predation is the most important, since incubating hen birds are very vulnerable and are easily caught by foxes hunting strips of nesting cover systematically. Because such predation removes the hen, no re-nesting is possible, and a single loss removes the potential of an entire brood. In the past the fox has always been cast in a villainous role by country people because of its depredations on livestock such as poultry and lambs. However foxes have thrived in most of Britain, and they never suffered the severe population decline which many of the other carnivores experienced in the 19th century. Undoubtedly this was because of the protection afforded by the organised fox hunts.

Since the abolition of gin traps, the principal methods used by gamekeepers to take foxes have been gassing earths, snaring, and shooting at night with a rifle. The last of these methods is becoming more widespread, as it is efficient, selective, and more humane than other methods. Despite this, gamekeepers find foxes difficult to control and the illegal use of poison still continues in some areas.

In counties with a high proportion of moorland fewest foxes are killed (Fig 23.1), and such areas are known to have a lower fox density than lowland districts (Hewson, 1986). The highest numbers killed are in southern England, with over 5 per 100 hectares per annum on Surrey shoots (Fig 23.1). This may be because neighbouring suburban areas support high densities of foxes, but also perhaps because young urban foxes are dispersing into rural areas (Page, 1981). Fox density in urban areas can reach up to 5 families per 100 hectares (Harris & Rayner, 1986), some 30 times the density of Dorset arable farmland (J.C. Reynolds & S.C. Tapper, unpublished).

Foxes were not listed on our census form until 1976, nevertheless they were frequently recorded in the space for extras. Where fox earths were gassed, contributors were asked to count one earth gassed as one fox. Fig

23.2 shows that the number killed has been increasing since 1961. This trend is apparent before and after 1976, and Fig 23.3 shows that this is true in most regions— particularly in southern and eastern England. We think this represents a real increase in the fox population, partly because this confirms the general impression of many gamekeepers, but also because other independent sources suggest the same. Lloyd (1980) showed that fox destruction societies in Wales killed an increasing number of foxes between 1948 and 1978. Hewson (1984) showed that Forestry Commission Conservancies in Scotland also took an increasing number between 1961 and 1978. Importantly, Kolb & Hewson (1980) demonstrated that the number of foxes killed could be related to the number of fox faeces they found—indicating that predator records are likely to reflect fox abundance.

Levels of fox abundance before 1961 are uncertain, and it is not clear just what impact myxomatosis in rabbits had on foxes. Certainly their diet, which contained more than 50% rabbits and hares prior to myxomatosis, changed to include more alternative foods (Lever, 1959); so it is probable that they were less affected than other species such as stoats. The large numbers of dead and dying rabbits during the outbreak of the disease may have produced a temporary excess of food which benefited fox production (Hewson & Kolb, 1973). However, records from one Suffolk estate suggest that myxomatosis did cause a short-term reduction in fox numbers, at least in East Anglia (Fig 23.4).

As well as becoming more numerous, foxes have also spread into areas where they had previously been scarce or absent. Examples include; suburban and urban areas (Harris & Rayner, 1986), some lowland parishes in north-east Scotland (Hewson & Kolb, 1973), the Fens, and north-west Norfolk. Foxes were certainly scarce in Norfolk until the early 1960's, and there were very few reported by gamekeepers in the early years of the census from much of East Anglia. Fig 23.5 suggests that by the 1960's foxes were already invading northwards through Thetford Forest and the country to the east. By the 1980's they were clearly abundant everywhere.

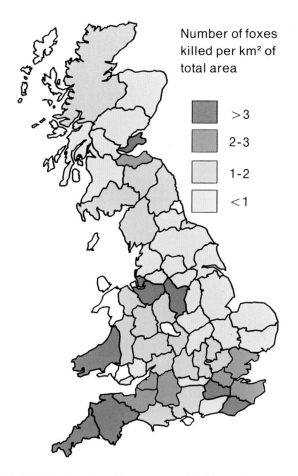

Number of foxes killed per km² of total area

▓ (dark)	> 3
▒ (medium)	2 - 3
░ (light)	1 - 2
□ (white)	< 1

Fig 23.1 Distribution of the average kill of foxes between 1961 and 1985.

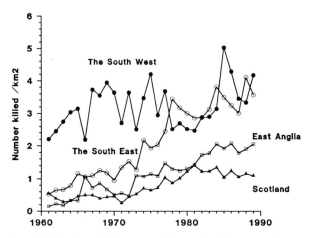

Fig 23.2 Trend in the average kill of foxes since 1961.

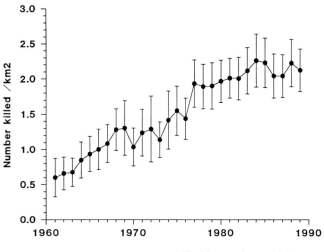

The South West

The South East

East Anglia

Scotland

Fig 23.3 Regional differences in the rate of increase in foxes killed since 1961.

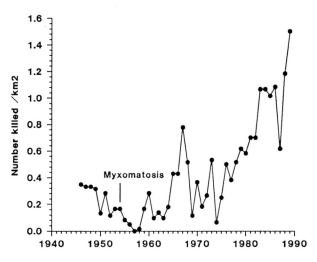

Myxomatosis

Fig 23.4 Changes in the numbers of foxes killed on a Suffolk estate, showing a temporary reduction in numbers after myxomatosis.

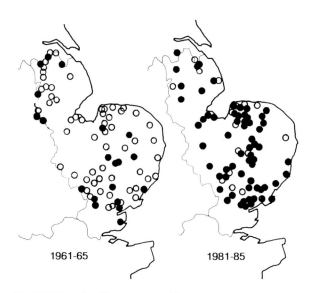

1961-65

1981-85

Fig 23.5 East Anglian estates which, on average, killed less than one fox per 1000 hectares (open circles) compared those that killed more (closed circles) for two comparable periods.

Grey Squirrel *(Sciurus carolinensis)*

The grey squirrel is a native of broadleaf forests in the eastern and central United States. Its natural range overlaps slightly with the North American red squirrel *(Tamiasciurus)*, and along the boundary the greys stick mainly to the deciduous woodland while the reds prefer conifers. In Britain the native red squirrel *(Sciurus vulgaris)* once inhabited both types of woodland, but it is probably much better adapted to conifers than broadleaves. Thus it is not entirely surprising that the introduced grey has largely taken over this habitat and their distribution and abundance today (reflected in the bag record—Fig 24.1) very much follows the proportion of broadleaved trees in British woodlands (Locke, 1987).

Although gamekeepers regard grey squirrels as potential egg predators, they are primarily killed because of the damage they cause to forest and woodland. In private woodlands their control is usually the job of the gamekeeper. Most tree damage is to hardwood species like beech and sycamore, and it occurs in spring when squirrels will strip bark from the trunks of rapidly growing trees between 20 and 40 years old. These seem to be the most vulnerable and there is a good relationship between the depth of the phloem layer (sap wood) and the likelihood of damage (Kenward & Parish, 1986). Actual squirrel numbers are very much influenced by the food supply in woodlands and there is no doubt that large quantities of food provided for released pheasants could considerably exacerbate the problem (Kenward, Parish & Robertson, 1992).

Methods of control have altered a lot since the squirrel problem first became apparent between the wars.

Initially shooting and tunnel trapping were the only methods available, but later—with the start of the "Anti-Grey Squirrel Campaign" in 1931—new types of cage traps were introduced and the development of the drey-poking pole made shooting more effective. After the second war, free cartridges were issued for squirrel control, and in 1953 a "shilling-a-tail" bounty scheme was introduced. None of these methods were adequate to curtail the spread or reduce the national abundance of squirrels and the Government eventually abandoned the idea of eradication and left it to landowners and the Forestry Commission to deal with squirrels as best they could. In recent years the most significant change has been the introduction of Warfarin poisoning under the Agriculture (Miscellaneous Provisions) Act 1972 and the Grey Squirrel (Warfarin) Order 1973.

The numbers killed nationally (Fig 24.2) show no clear long-term trend, but there is considerable short-term variation, some of which is undoubtedly influenced by changing methods of control. For example the use of poison will lead to more unrecorded kills. However, some variation is due to fluctuating beech mast and acorn crops which, in 1977 for example, resulted in high squirrel densities (Gurnell, 1987).

The original introductions of grey squirrels were made around the turn of the century, and Middleton (1931) lists some 32 separate occasions when they were released, sometimes from new American stock but also from previously established colonies in England. Most of these introductions seemed not to be for any sporting purpose, but purely because estate owners liked to have an exotic species around in their country parks. From these early colonies, sizeable population centres were established within 10 to 20 years (Fig 24.3). Within another decade these populations were beginning to coalesce, and a large tract of countryside from Kent to Staffordshire was occupied. In 1945 most of central and southern England was occupied and squirrels were pushing into Wales and the west country (Shorten, 1954). By the 1960's the animal's present day range was almost complete. Only one major area, East Anglia, has been colonised since. Why this area should have remained free of grey squirrels until recently is not clear, though undoubtedly the Ouse washes and fen country cut off invasion from the north-west. When the invasion did take place it did so from the south, and it occurred comparatively quickly, as is clearly shown by gamekeepers' bag returns. Fig 24.4 shows the bag for East Anglia, indicating a rising trend not yet reaching an asymptote. Fig 24.5 shows the localities of estates recording grey squirrels for 4 separate years and highlights a line of invasion from Essex, through west Suffolk and into north west Norfolk. The invasion of Norfolk has been documented in detail by Reynolds (1985).

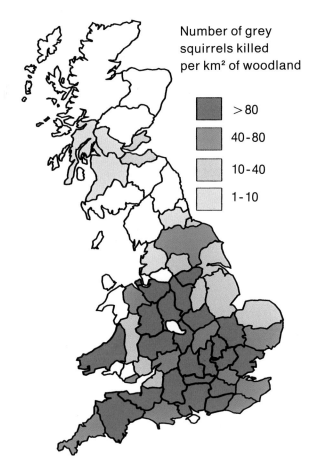

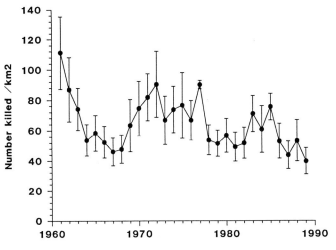

Fig 24.2 Trend in the average kill of grey squirrels since 1961.

Fig 24.1 Distribution of the average kill of grey squirrels between 1961 and 1985.

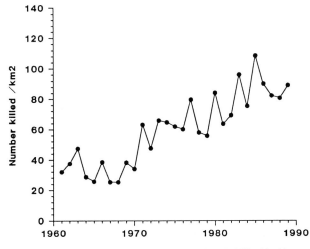

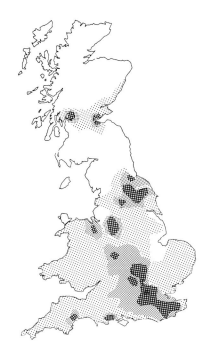

Fig 24.3 Spread in the range of the grey squirrel. Dark stipple = before 1920; medium stipple = by 1930; light stipple = by 1983. From Middleton (1931) & Arnold (1984).

Fig 24.4 Rise in the number of grey squirrels killed in East Anglia since 1961.

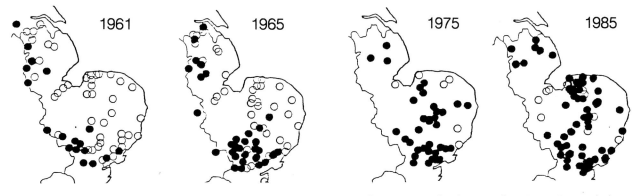

Fig 24.5 Distribution of estates which submitted pest control records where grey squirrels were absent or not recorded (open circles) and those where they were recorded (black dots).

Brown Rat *(Rattus norvegicus)*

The brown rat has been one of the most successful colonists of the British Isles. Introduced into Britain through the trade routes to central Asia, it became established in the mid 18th century. Since then it has largely displaced the black rat *(Rattus rattus)* which came in the 11th century. The brown rat is more adapted to life outdoors than the black, and so is better able to exploit man's farming activities. Brown rats are therefore a serious agricultural pest and the need for rat control arises from agricultural loss in the field and in stored produce, rather than the need for disease prevention. Some agricultural methods, in particular the practise of storing corn in ricks, provided an ideal breeding ground for rats, and arable areas have always had more rats than upland or grassland districts. This is also evident in keepers records (Fig 25.1).

War time work by the Bureau of Animal Population showed that rats could breed all winter in corn ricks and infestations gradually increased the longer the rick was left. The average population per rick was 17 in early winter, but over 70 by spring (Venables & Leslie, 1942). In one case over 500 rats were found in a single rick (Matheson, 1962). So important was the corn rick as a harbourage for rats that it was made illegal to break up a stack without first fencing it with wire netting to contain the dispersing rats (Prevention of Damage by Pests—Threshing and Dismantling of Ricks Regulations 1950).

On most estates the job of controlling rats has been left to the keepers. Apart from the terriers which they kept for dealing with both foxes and rats, traps and snares were the main methods used before the second war. The rat snare was usually a "bender", a snare set in a run and attached to a bent piece of ash or hazel which would spring upwards, hanging the rat in the noose. These methods accounted for huge numbers rats and indeed over 80% of the vermin killed on one estate before the first war comprised rats (Fig 25.3). However, the revolution in rat control which took place in the 1940's and 1950's resulted not only in fewer rats, but in fewer being recorded (Fig 25.3).

This revolution in rat control originated during the second war when agricultural production was paramount. Post-war losses to rats were estimated at £25,000,000 annually, with most due to damage and spoiling of stored grain (Lancum, 1951). Intensive research at the Oxford Bureau and the Ministry of Agriculture eventually led to the use of poisoning on a wide scale. A key finding was the discovery of "the new object reaction", by which rats avoid anything unusual in their environment for several days. Thus a first reaction to a poisoned bait was avoidance, followed perhaps by a cautious taste. Consequently early attempts at poisoning were ineffective. The new approach was to pre-bait at specific sites, so rats became accustomed to feeding stations. By using small rations, rats would compete with one another to get to food and so develop the habit of not tasting first. A few days later the food was laced with poison. War-time campaigns against rats using these methods were extremely effective and in one operation over 1000 men were employed to poison the London sewers. The advent of such methods of control meant that most rats died underground and could not be counted. Thus paradoxically as control became more efficient an index based on rats killed and counted became less reliable, and the total number of kills counted actually declined (Fig 25.4).

By the mid 1950's the poisoning methods took another step forward with the discovery of anti-coagulant poisons. First discovered when an American farmer found his cattle dying from eating coumarin-rich alfalfa, the product Warfarin first became available commercially in the early 1960's. The main advantage of anticoagulants was that baits could be laid out continuously, and rats would learn to feed regularly at these sites before succumbing to the effects of the poison. This improvement in control is undoubtedly the reason why the average number of rats recorded killed has continued to decline (Fig 25.2).

Modern methods rely on the use of various anticoagulant poisons, but still the main period for control is the winter when rats are concentrated around farm buildings or other places with access to food and shelter (Fig 25.5). Those killed in the summer are usually taken in Fenn traps or shot by the keeper during his daily rounds.

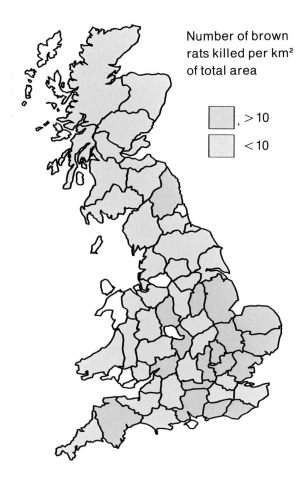

Number of brown
rats killed per km²
of total area

, > 10

< 10

Fig 25.1 Distribution of the average kill of rats between
1961 and 1985

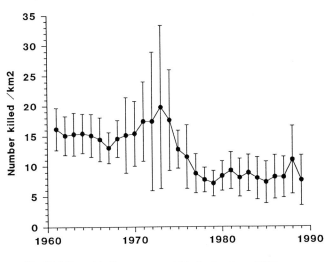

Fig 25.2 Trend in the average kill of rats since 1961

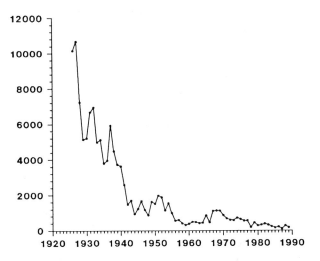

Fig 25.4 Total numbers of rats recorded killed by the
gamekeepers on an East Anglian estate since 1926.

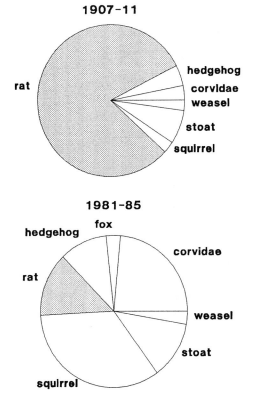

1907–11

rat

hedgehog
corvidae
weasel
stoat
squirrel

1981–85

fox
hedgehog
rat
corvidae
weasel
stoat
squirrel

Fig 25.3 Number of rats killed on a Suffolk estate as a
proportion of the total number of pests and predators
(excluding rabbits) pre World War I (above), and today
(below).

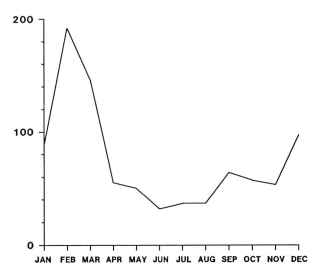

Fig 25.5 Average number of rats killed per month on a
Sussex downland shoot in the early 1970's.

Magpie *(Pica pica)*

A social yet territorial corvid, the magpie is a bird of scrub and edge habitats, which has adapted well to the hedgerow and patchwork countryside of England (Birkhead, 1991). Its diet is omnivorous (Holyoak, 1968), and it will take grain as readily as it will kill a mouse. On farmland much of its time is spent in permanent pasture foraging for insects (Holyoak, 1974), and some foods may be temporarily cached. However, it is also alert enough to take advantage of the seasonal abundance of eggs and nestlings in spring. Indeed, Holyoak (1968) found gamebird eggs in 23% of magpies taken by gamekeepers on farmland in May and June—however in this case one wonders whether many of the eggs were not in fact being used by gamekeepers as bait. Although magpies are territorial in spring and summer, this does not appear to restrict their density, and nests have been found as little as 87 metres apart. Many birds, particularly first year animals, will remain in the population as non-breeders (Holyoak, 1974).

Of all the gamebird predators, the magpie is arguably the most disliked by lowland gamekeepers. Not only is it exceedingly quick to take a vulnerable nest, it is equally rapid at making itself scarce when the keeper is around. Being highly visible it also advertises to the landowner that the keeper is perhaps not doing his job properly. Equally frustrating from the keeper's point of view is the fact there often seems to be an unending succession of replacements for the birds he does get rid of.

The methods used by keepers to take magpies have been many and various. A good number are accounted for with the shot gun, and in the past it is probable that many were taken illegally using alphachloralose obtained for controlling rats and mice in farm buildings. In spite of the dangers of such methods, keepers persisted in using them because they were simple and effective. However, magpie control is feasible without such techniques, and the simple Larsen trap, designed with

two compartments so that one captured bird entices down another, can be extremely efficient. In Denmark where this trap was invented, Strandgaard & Asferg (1980) attribute the declining bag in that country since 1967 to a reducing magpie population brought about by trapping.

The distribution of the bag (Fig 26.1) suggests a higher overall abundance in the south of England than in the north, and densities in Scotland are particularly low. This corresponds with both the breeding distribution and wintering density of this species (Birkhead, 1986; Sharrock, 1976). Fig 26.3 shows this clearly, and represents magpies as a proportion of other territorial corvids taken by keepers in the east; from the south where 37% of the corvids are magpies, to Scotland where only 3% are magpies. Moreover, the high numbers in the counties which fringe the urban and suburban areas suggest a parallel with the fox, where the progeny of town animals which live off bird table scraps and garden refuse may invade neighbouring farmland. Clarkson & Birkhead (1987) have recorded a massive increase in numbers in the Sheffield area. Certainly the national trend (Fig 26.2) indicates a steady increase, but it hides the variation between areas. Fig 26.4 shows three regions, indicating little change in the south west, an increase in recent years in East Anglia, and an almost fourfold explosion in numbers in the south east. The increase in birds taken surely represents the numbers alive as it also parallels Common Bird Census data (Fig 26.5), as well as a rising tide of complaints not only from game preservers but also garden bird lovers who watch magpies ransack nesting chaffinches and blackbirds with monotonous regularity. However, nesting and fledging success of songbirds has not deteriorated during the years of magpie increase, and there is no sound evidence yet that song-birds are suffering as a consequence of a growth in magpie predation (Gooch, Baillie & Birkhead, 1991).

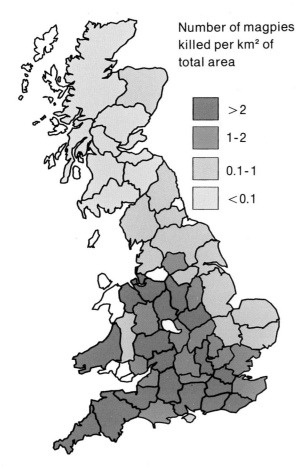

Number of magpies killed per km² of total area

■ >2
▨ 1-2
▧ 0.1-1
□ <0.1

Fig 26.1 Distribution of the average kill of magpies between 1961-1985.

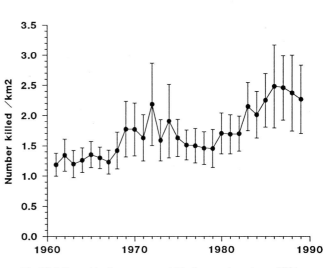

Fig 26.2 Trend in the average kill of magpies since 1961.

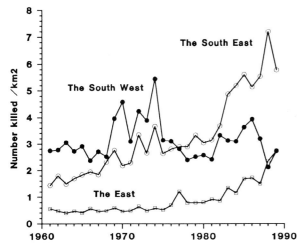

Fig 26.4 Trend in numbers of magpies killed in 3 different regions.

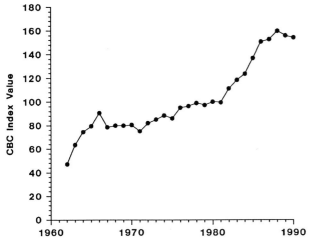

Fig 26.5 British Trust for Ornithology's Common Bird Census for the magpie. Farmland sites only.

Eastern Scotland

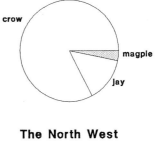

The North West

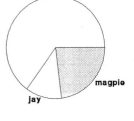

East Anglia

The South East

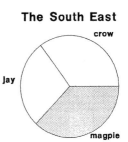

Fig 26.3 Proportion of magpies in relation to other territorial corvids taken by gamekeepers in 4 areas.

Carrion and Hooded Crow *(Corvus corone)*

Hooded and carrion crows are now considered the same species, although geographically they are largely distinct. It is thought that the two types originated during the Pleistocene, when crows were pushed south by the ice sheet into two refuge populations in Iberia and the Balkans. As the ice retreated the populations came together again but have remained distinct races with different ranges even though they do hybridise along their boundaries. In Britain, this boundary roughly separates the "hoodies" in the north-west Highlands along the line of the Great Glen, from the "carrions" in the rest of Britain (Sharrock, 1976). This boundary has been moving north-west to this position since at least the 1920's (Cook, 1975).

Crows are large and highly territorial corvids found commonly in most habitats in Britain. Populations also contain many non-territorial and non-breeding birds, and these can often be found in large flocks driven off by resident pairs. There is little doubt that territoriality does limit the breeding density of crows (Charles, 1972).

Crows are omnivores, feeding on insects and grain as well as carrion and nestlings (Holyoak, 1968). They are adept nest robbers, particularly of ground nesting birds and will sit on fence posts or in hedgerow trees watching for partridges leaving nests. Potts (1986) found over 260 gamebird eggs at one crow nest in Sussex over two years.

This egg-eating habit makes crows the most important avian predator of gamebirds. Until the recent introduction of the Larsen trap they have been difficult to control, since they easily avoid a patrolling gamekeeper and are wary of many types of cage trap. An effective method is to wait until the territorial pairs have nested, allowing them to drive away the flocks of non-territorial birds, and only to remove the residents when the gamebirds themselves have begun to nest. Killing the residents can still be a problem, but shooting with a rifle is effective, as is shooting out the nest and the adult birds with a shotgun on a windy night. Crow control by these means is extremely labour intensive and relies on good field craft. Unfortunately, with keepers now being expected to undertake larger game rearing programmes, the time needed for these methods is not often available. In the recent past keepers have sometimes resorted to undesirable and illegal methods—in particular the use of poison (Bunyan *et al.*, 1975).

The distribution of the bag of the two races (Figs 27.1 & 27.2) corresponds well with their winter abundance (Houston, 1986), with "carrions" being noticeably less common in East Anglia and Scotland. The presence of "hoodies" along the east of England coast probably reflects immigrant wintering birds from Scandinavia. However the proportion of these birds in the bag is very small and they are only significant in Scotland (Fig 27.3).

The trend in numbers of both races is shown in Fig 27.4 and would suggest that "carrion" numbers have remained virtually constant since 1960, whereas "'hoodies" have substantially increased. This is in marked contrast to the British Trust for Ornithology's Common Bird Census (Fig 27.5) which suggests a steady and large increase in crow numbers. There is no clear explanation for this divergence. Perhaps numbers have increased but keepers are simply unable to deal with more than a few birds each year. Conversely, the number of birds settling on keepered estates may not have changed, but a declining number of keepered areas in proximity to Common Bird Census sites may mean that unkeepered farmland does now support higher populations.

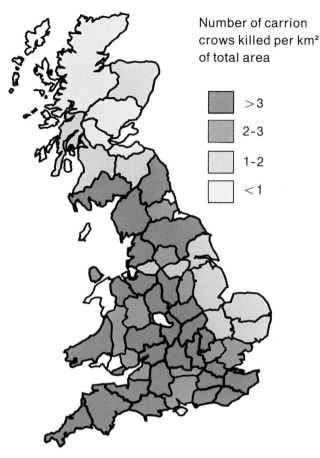

Number of carrion crows killed per km² of total area

▓▓ (dark)	>3
▒▒ (medium)	2-3
░░ (light)	1-2
□□ (white)	<1

Fig 27.1 Distribution in the average kill of carrion crows between 1961 and 1985.

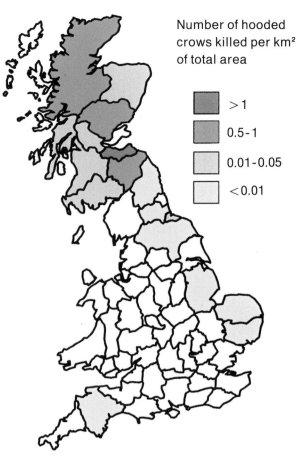

Number of hooded crows killed per km² of total area

▓▓ (dark)	>1
▒▒ (medium)	0.5-1
░░ (light)	0.01-0.05
□□ (white)	<0.01

Fig 27.2 Distribution in the average kill of hooded crows between 1961 and 1985.

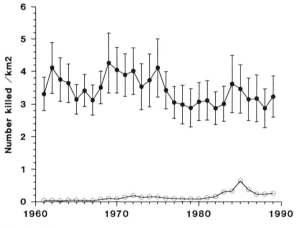

Fig 27.4 Trend in the average kill of carrion (upper line) in all Britain and hooded crows (lower line) in Scotland since 1961.

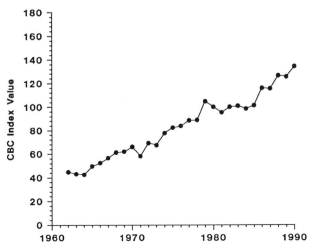

Fig 27.5 British Trust for Ornithology's Common Bird Census for carrion crows from farmland sites.

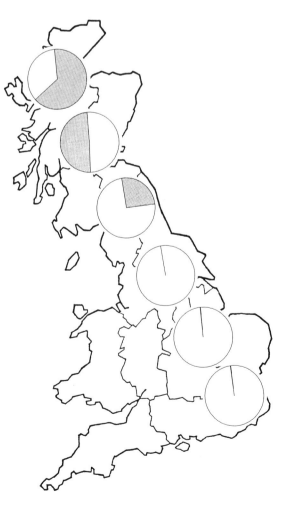

Fig 27.3 The proportion of "hoodies" in the crow bag in certain counties; Highlands, Tayside, Borders, North Yorkshire, Lincolnshire, and Suffolk.

Rook *(Corvus frugilegus)*

The most gregarious of Britain's corvids, the rook, is a species that has adapted well to the mixed arable farming system that has evolved over much of our lowland landscape. Their leisurely flights across the evening sky to a distant roost are a common feature of the English countryside, just as their noisy nest building arguments in the upper branches of bare February trees are among the first encouraging signs that the year has turned and winter is nearly over.

To the farmer, rooks can be an irritating pest and when large flocks settle on his land to feed they represent a threat to his crops (Feare, 1974). However, since rooks are mainly insectivorous birds (Fog, 1963; Feare, Dunnet & Patterson, 1974), the crop damage they inflict is nothing like as serious as would be done by an equivalent number of rabbits. Nevertheless they can be a considerable nuisance—particularly to spring sown corn. Rooks will also pull out newly planted potatoes and in the autumn trample and eat ripening corn, especially if it is already partly lodged. Because rooks can fly in from some distance to feed, this can make control difficult if the farmer does not have access to the rookery or roost site. As a result many farmers resort to scaring devices such as flapping fertiliser bags or gas-bangers. The effectiveness of these can be rather limited (Feare, 1974).

The rook is also regarded as a potential egg thief by the gamekeeper, and although he would not consider them as serious a threat as magpies or carrion crows, there are plenty of instances which show that, given the opportunity, rooks will steal eggs. On rearing fields for example, rooks will quickly learn to take eggs from un-netted laying pens. Likewise on old-fashioned partridge beats using the Euston system (see page 36) large numbers of dummy eggs have been found beneath rookeries, providing conclusive proof of the rooks' activities. Although a gamekeeper is unlikely to attempt to eradicate all rooks each spring, he will certainly try to thin their numbers considerably. If he can get at the

rookery, he can do this by disturbing them at night while the hen birds are incubating, so causing desertion and egg chilling. Later he can shoot the young rooks (branchers) with a .22 calibre rifle as they fledge. For the adults, cage trapping and shooting birds as they fly in to roost are appropriate techniques. As with other corvids a proportion have been taken illegally with poison.

The regional distribution of the bag (Fig 28.1) reflects this bird's preference for mixed farmland. Numbers are higher, for example, in central southern counties than they are in East Anglia, which tends to have more intensive arable. This distribution roughly corresponds to that of the wintering population and the density of rookeries (Brenchley, 1986; Sage & Vernon, 1978).

The British Trust for Ornithology has conducted periodic surveys of rookeries and the game bag data provides an interesting comparison. The trend for Britain indicates a steady reduction in numbers between 1969 and 1982, with a partial recovery in recent years (Fig 28.2). However this hides important regional differences. For example, East Anglia and the south east both show the decline but a recovery is only partially evident in the south east (Fig 28.3). By contrast Scotland and the south west show no decline (Fig 28.4). These results reflect changes in rook breeding numbers between 1975 and 1980 (Sage & Whittington, 1985; Fig 28.5), and earlier (Sage & Vernon, 1978).

The cause of the rook decline, which probably followed a post-war increase, may be intensive arable farming and the decline of the traditional cereal/grass ley rotation. Certainly the reduction in temporary grasslands (important feeding areas for rooks on farmland) in East Anglia corresponds with the decline (Fig 28.6). It is likely that the loss of elm trees has had only a minor effect, and it probably caused a fragmentation of rookeries rather than a decline in the actual number of nests (Osborne, 1982).

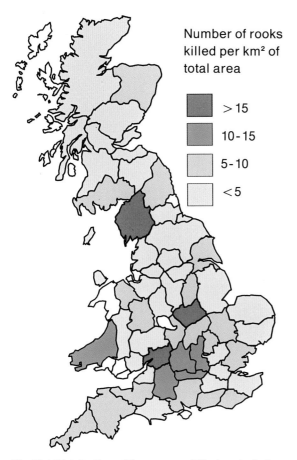

Number of rooks
killed per km² of
total area

■	> 15
▨	10 - 15
▤	5 - 10
□	< 5

Fig 28.1 Distribution of the average kill of rooks between 1961 and 1985.

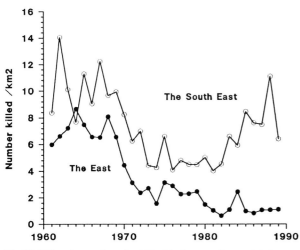

The South East

The East

Fig 28.3 Numbers of rooks killed in two regions which have shown a decline since 1961.

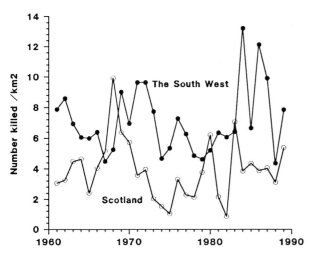

The South West

Scotland

Fig 28.4 Numbers of rooks killed in two regions which have not shown a decline since 1961.

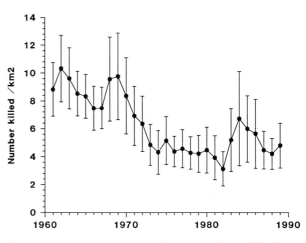

Fig 28.2 Trend in the average kill of rooks from all Britain since 1961.

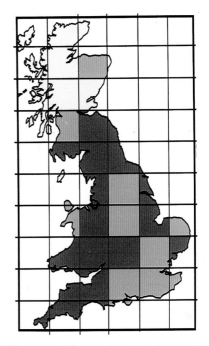

Fig 28.5 Changes in the number of rook nests between 1975 and 1980 shown by the British Trust for Ornithology's rookery surveys. From Sage & Whittington (1985). Brown = increased number of nests. Blue = decreased number.

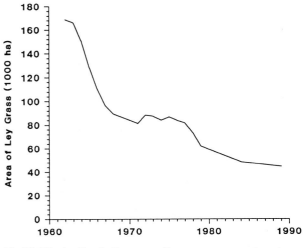

Fig 28.6 Reduction in the area of temporary grass leys in East Anglia. From Ministry of Agriculture.

Jackdaw *(Corvus monedula)*

Like the rook, the jackdaw is a gregarious and colonial, rather than territorial, corvid. To countrymen jackdaws have always appeared to be playful creatures, particularly in spring as they tumble about the sky in strong March winds. The smart grey plumage on their heads and their bright steely eyes give them a cheeky rather than malevolent appearance. Further, they are the most commensal of all the crow family, often nesting in old buildings, rooves, and attics, and sometimes flapping down chimneys into living rooms at inconvenient moments.

Farmland jackdaws are mainly insectivorous, foraging in flocks on pastures, leys and stubbles. These feeding flocks are often in association with large numbers of rooks. In fact rooks and jackdaws have very similar habits and food requirements. In winter mixed flocks will often fly back to roost in the same woods, but the two species usually choose to settle in different trees. From the farmer's point of view jackdaws are perhaps rather less damaging to crops than rooks, but the gamekeeper will regard jackdaws as more likely to learn the whereabouts of a gamebird nest or the presence of eggs in a rearing pen.

The similarity with rooks is reflected in the game bag records. The overall distribution of kills is broadly the same, with most being taken in the mixed arable farmland and wooded counties of southern England and the midlands. There are notably fewer in East Anglia and the north (Fig 29.1). In a similar way to the rook, the bag has shown a steady reduction since the early 1960's (Fig 29.2). The jackdaw's decline is just as marked and nationally appears to have recovered less than the rook. Like the rook there are regional differences too (Fig 29.3). However, the rate of decline in East Anglia appears to have been slightly faster for the rook than the jackdaw (Fig 29.4).

A possible cause for the decline of both species may be the change in arable farming over the last twenty-five years. In the 1950's and early 1960's most cereals were grown in rotation with grass which would have been undersown as a ley into the last crop of barley. The grass ley would be left for two to three years and used either for hay or as grazing for livestock such as a beef herd. This farming system produced a patchwork arable landscape that provided insect rich feeding areas in grass fields at all times of the year in addition to grain on cereal stubbles and a temporary flush of worms and grubs at ploughing time. With the intensification of cereal production in the 1960's and 1970's, rotations were simplified so that grass leys and their associated livestock were omitted, to be replaced with break crops such as oilseed rape or beans. These latter crops are drilled and harvested at roughly the same time as cereals, so the landscape looses its habitat diversity and becomes structurally homogeneous. All crops are harvested in late summer. There is rapid clearance of all stubbles by burning, followed by cultivation and drilling of virtually all fields by the autumn. Such farmland provides few places for insect foraging in summer and spring when jackdaws and rooks have to feed their young. However, in general, jackdaws do fare better on arable farmland than they do on pasture, and O'Conner & Shrub (1986) have shown that egg and nestling losses are much lower on arable farms than in other habitats.

There is no adequate explanation for the marked difference between the bag record of jackdaws, and the Common Bird Census index which has shown a marked increase since at least the mid 1970's. However jackdaws are colonial nesters and as a result are difficult to monitor accurately with the normal census methods. (Fig 29.5).

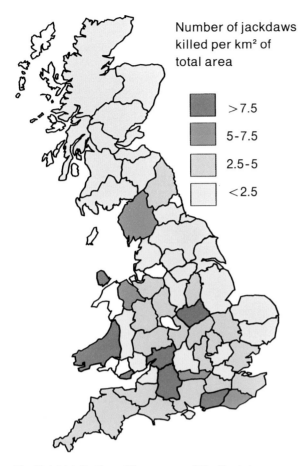

Number of jackdaws
killed per km² of
total area

> 7.5
5 - 7.5
2.5 - 5
< 2.5

Fig 29.1 Distribution of the average kill of jackdaws
between 1961 and 1985.

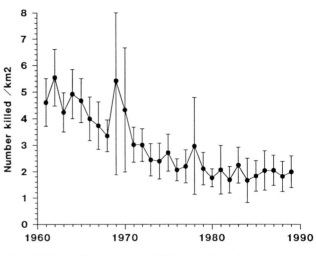

Fig 29.2 Trend in the average kill of jackdaws from all
Britain since 1961.

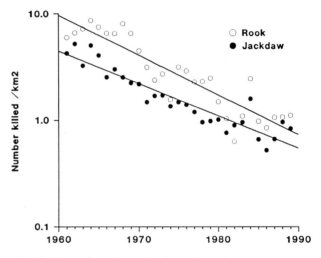

○ Rook
● Jackdaw

Fig 29.4 Rate of decline in the bag of jackdaws compared
with rooks in East Anglia.

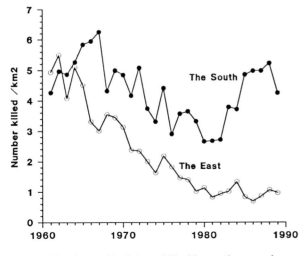

The South

The East

Fig 29.3 Numbers of jackdaws killed in southern and
eastern regions since 1961.

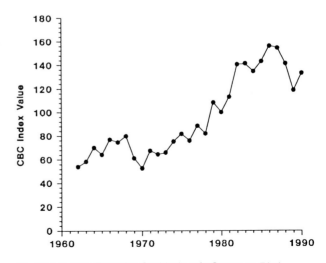

Fig 29.5 British Trust for Ornithology's Common Bird
Census for jackdaws from farmland sites.

95

Jay *(Garrulus glandarius)*

With its smart pinky-grey plumage the jay is Britain's most attractive corvid, and it is certainly the least damaging from a gamekeepers point of view. In spring, it is a bit of nest robber, but the few eggs and chicks that it does take are usually from small song birds rather than pheasant or partridge nests. Many keepers also regard the jay as a useful ally, as its raucous warning cry is easily triggered when disturbed. Thus a keeper patrolling his beat will be warned of the unwelcome intrusion of a fox or poacher in a nearby covert by the jay's noisy call.

One may therefore wonder why such a species should appear on the vermin list at all. However, there are plenty of instances where jays have been recorded taking game; occasionally pheasant eggs, but more commonly young chicks, particularly where they are exposed on a rearing field and under the very eye of the keeper. Another reason for shooting the odd jay is that its bright blue wing coverts are important ingredients in some classic salmon fly patterns (e.g. Thunder and Lightning, and Black Doctor). Although the price paid for jay wings, or indeed any other animal bits and pieces such as woodcock and starling wings, or squirrel and stoat tails barely covers the cost of cartridges, many keepers do collect these items to give to friends or sell to tackle dealers each year. However, most of the jays that are shot are probably not taken by the gamekeeper at all but by guns on pheasant shooting days. The odd jay that comes forward during a woodland pheasant drive provides an interesting diversion from the more predictable pheasants. Perhaps one might consider the jay as a part-time gamebird.

The jay is a bird of the deciduous forest and their optimum habitat in Britain is the oak woodland of the south. This is reflected in the distribution of the bag (Fig 30.1) which shows a marked concentration in the heavily wooded counties of southern England, where oak rather than ash is the climax forest. There is a clear correlation between the bag and the area of woodland on shoots, even within a single region (Fig 30.3).

The overall bag has not changed much since the early 1960's (Fig 30.2), but it does seem more variable than the changes noted by the Common Bird Census (Fig 30.4). But, as discussed above, most jays are probably taken during winter pheasant shoots so our data reflect winter populations more than the spring ones recorded in the bird census. Jays are normally resident birds and winter numbers usually reflect the breeding distribution (John, 1986; Sharrock, 1976). However, there are occasions when migrations do seem to occur. In October 1983 large numbers of jays were reported in the south at various sites from Dover to Lands End, where one flock of over 3000 was seen. Smaller flocks were also seen along the east coast (John & Roskell, 1985). Many of these were continental birds, and may have been part of a general westward migration which occasionally takes place. Failure of the acorn crop is believed to be the main cause for these invasions. This particular invasion seems to have been short-lived as the Common Bird Census index shows no increase in 1984 numbers. The game bag data, however, do reflect the migrations and in East Anglia and the east midlands the numbers shot were the highest ever recorded (Fig 30.5).

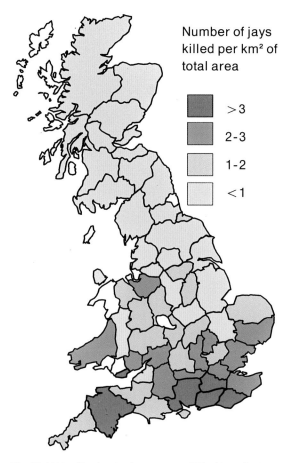

Number of jays
killed per km² of
total area

■	> 3
▨	2-3
▧	1-2
□	< 1

Fig 30.1 Distribution in the average kill of jays between 1961-85.

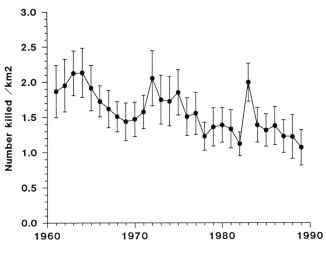

Fig 30.2 Trend in the average kill of jays from all Britain since 1961.

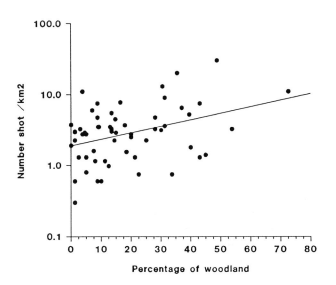

Fig 30.3 Correlation between the numbers of jays shot on shoots in the south west region in 1983, and the proportion of the shoot area that is woodland.

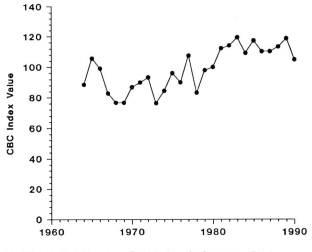

Fig 30.4 British Trust for Ornithology's Common Bird Census for jays from woodland sites.

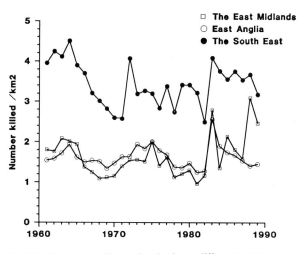

Fig 30.5 Numbers of jays shot in three different areas since 1961.

97

AN OVERVIEW

Then and Now: Edwardians and Elizabethans

Thirty seven species have been examined in this volume and in many cases their fortunes have been traced over much of this century. For each bird or mammal there has been a different story to tell, and although the records mirror changing abundance they are in part also a reflection of other factors, such as fashion or species protection. Some game species, for example the deer, birds of the shoreline, and geese are not considered, partly because they are often not recorded in game books, and partly because they have not formed part of the Game Conservancy's National Game Bag Census, which has concentrated on small game and their related predators. Equally there are little or no data on the legally protected predatory species; badgers, otters, hawks and owls, which gamekeepers have undoubtedly killed in the past but have naturally been shy of recording. Except for the lingering effects of organochlorine pesticides and pollutant PCB's, which have had a more devastating effect on some species than any force of gamekeepers, most of these predators have increased in abundance and range. None are now threatened by continued persecution from gamekeepers.

Let us see first how the shooting bag as a whole has changed this century. We can do this by looking at those estates which were recording game bags in 1900 and are still doing so today. They are only a small proportion of the total, and certainly would be those inclined towards more traditional management methods compared to shoots of more recent origin. We can draw up a summary table of head of game shot per kilometre square, comparing the Edwardians of the turn of the century with our present day Elizabethans (Table 31.1).

Clearly the upland estates have suffered a large drop in the wild game bag due to the collapse of the grouse species in Scotland. Obviously there is a large variation between moors, and the reduction of over 50% suggested by the above table does not hold true everywhere. In fact, bags on some moors have gone to almost zero, while others, including the large well managed estates in the north of England, have maintained high levels of productivity. There is no doubt however, that many places eventually reach a point where the bags are simply not large enough to justify the upkeep of the moor and the employment of a gamekeeper. In such cases the landowner is likely to switch from grouse moor management to commercial forestry, foreclosing future game management prospects .

On the face of it the lowland estates are today doing quite well when compared with their Edwardian past.

Table 31.1 Head of game shot during two eras this century. Expressed as bag per kilometre square.

	Edwardians 1900-1909	New Elizabethans 1980-1989
Lowland Estates		
Pheasant	14.80	48.60
Grey partridge	27.50	5.50
Redleg partridge	0.82*	9.60
Woodcock	0.50	2.10
Common snipe	0.45	0.14
Brown hare	15.80	9.00
Rabbit	36.50	12.40
Total	96.37	87.34
Upland Estates		
Red grouse	58.59	26.23
Black grouse	0.59	0.03
Capercaillie	0.23	0.06
Mountain hare	2.03	1.08
Total	61.44	27.40

* Estimated as 3% of the grey partridge bag

Of course there are far fewer of them, and gamekeepered ground on which there is shooting is probably now only about a tenth of what it was in the Edwardian heyday. Most of the estates in our sample were once a good deal larger than today, so their total shooting bags were bigger too. But, per unit of ground the bag is 90% of what it was 80 years ago. However, there are some very fundamental differences. In 1900 most shooting was done by wealthy landowners and their friends, and there was, as we pointed out in the beginning of this account, a competitive spirit about the size of the bag made by individual guns. Edwardian shoots were often aimed at several very large days, sweeping in wide areas and beating in boundaries to achieve huge daily totals. Today, most estates cannot afford to run their shoot days entirely as private social occasions, and they have to devise ways of defraying the costs by letting individual beats to syndicate guns

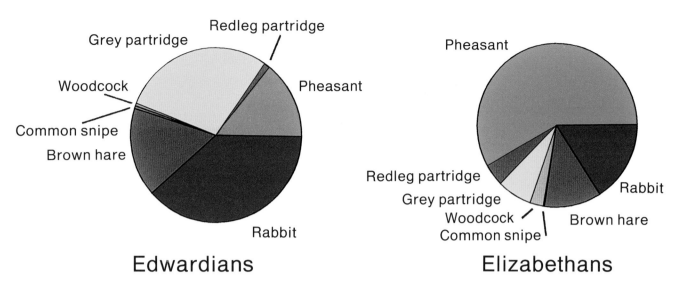

Fig 31.1 Proportion of different species represented in the game bag of selected estates with records available in the decade from 1900 (Edwardians) and from 1980 (Elizabethans).

or taking paying guests on a daily basis. The result is smaller shoots held more often.

But, more importantly, there is also a fundamental difference in the nature of the game bag in these two eras. Fig 31.1 shows the proportions of the different species that made up the bag on these estates. The increased emphasis today on pheasants is striking, but underlying this is the fact that most of these pheasants and the redleg partridges are hand-reared and released before the season opens. Although hand-rearing has always been the practice on many estates, levels used to be much lower since the old fashioned systems were very labour intensive and very expensive. In our sample of key estates where rearing is also recorded, there are almost ten times as many birds being hand-reared today as there were 80 years ago. Indeed most lowland shooting has now switched from a reliance on wild stock to a dependence on hand-reared birds.

This increased emphasis on pheasants now dominates lowland shooting today. We have estimated that about 12 million are shot annually and the bulk of these are derived from birds that have been hand-reared. Leaving aside species like rabbits and woodpigeons which are taken to a large extent by farmers and others for pest control, the total wild game bag today for different species can be calculated from our estimates of numbers shot per hundred hectares and from the estimated proportion of ground that is shot over (based on Piddington, 1981). We can do a similar exercise with our data from the early part of this century by using the numbers shot per hundred hectares, knowing the number of gamekeepers employed from the national census and assuming an average size beat for each keeper. The results are shown in Fig 31.2 and suggest that the Edwardians were shooting annually well over a million of several game species and in the case of the grey partridge over two million. Except for the pheasant, the

levels of shooting today are a fraction of what they were. The pheasant increase we can safely attribute to those hand-reared birds which survive shooting and eventually breed to produce wild young of their own. Thus the wild stock is being constantly topped up by the rearing programme. On a smaller scale the same is true for redleg partridge. On this basis the only true increase in the bag of a wild game species is the woodcock.

The switch from wild to hand-reared game in the lowlands has largely been forced upon landowners by fundamental changes in agriculture. In earlier times it was the farmland countryside which nurtured the birds all year round; providing the hedgerow nesting cover, the weedy cereal crops full of insects as food for growing chicks, and stubble fields left down until spring, covered with weed seeds and spilt grain as winter food. Nowadays clean arable systems provide little of this,

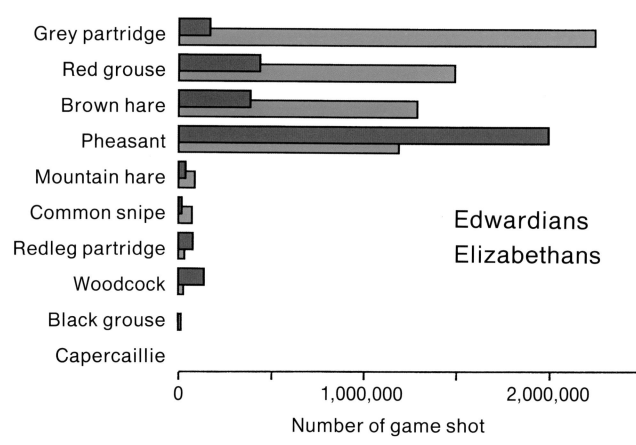

Grey partridge
Red grouse
Brown hare
Pheasant
Mountain hare
Common snipe
Redleg partridge
Woodcock
Black grouse
Capercaillie

0   1,000,000   2,000,000

Number of game shot

Edwardians
Elizabethans

Fig 31.2 Approximate estimates of the total national bag of a selection of important wild game species from the early part of this century (Edwardians) compared with a later part (Elizabethans). Pheasants and redleg partridges which are reared and released have been discounted.

so the solution has been for the gamekeeper to rear birds artificially. Pheasants can be raised in brooder houses, fed on high protein pelleted food, and released into areas with grain-filled feeder-hoppers. So the environmental prerequisites to run a modern shoot are much lower than for a shoot based on wild game. Some shoots now exist on bare arable farms where the only game cover is a few strips of kale or artichoke. In such situations the farm management is largely divorced from game conservation and indeed the gamekeeper is necessarily more concerned about the possibility of disease wiping out hundreds of pheasant poults than he is about the breeding success of wild birds in the hedgerow.

In spite of this, many landowners try to improve their ground for holding both reared and wild game by planting woods, retaining hedges and trying to adopt wild-life friendly techniques on the farmland that they control. The tragedy is, as we shall see, the wild game appears to have responded very little. In order to find out why, we must look at our wild species more closely and consider their population status rather than simply their contribution to the sportsman's bag. We can start by drawing up a balance sheet of all the mammals and birds considered in this review and see how they have fared in the post war era. Table 31.2 is an assessment of changing abundance (not the bag) of these species in the countryside, and for those species where birds

are hand-reared we have tried to assess what would have happened had there been no artificial rearing.

This analysis is inevitably a little simplistic; for example, woodpigeon went through a decline before increasing and some like jackdaw and rook, are probably now increasing again. Woodcock wintering numbers we have interpreted as stable, even though the bag is increasing, but breeding numbers are probably declining. The table takes no account of levels of abundance, and rare species in decline clearly warrant more concern than common species with the same trend. There are also question marks over some common species like the hedgehog where partial legal protection has led to fewer being killed and recorded by gamekeepers. Nevertheless it is apparent that the majority of wild game (except woodcock, waterfowl and those we class as agricultural pests) are declining, and many of the predatory species correspondingly increasing. It is natural to wonder whether or not the increase in predators has caused the decline in game. If this were true then it seems to be the reverse of what traditional ecology teaches; that is that *prey abundance governs the abundance of predators—not the other way round.*

There are at least three reasons why the small game community does not follow this theory. First, these animals are part of a man-managed system and man has always been a key predator both of the game and the other predators. Second, the game species are only

Table 31.2 A balance sheet of the populations of game and predator species considered in this book		
INCREASING	STABLE	DECLINING
I Small Game Species		
Mallard *	Mountain hare	Brown hare
Teal	Woodcock	Pheasant *
Tufted duck		Grey partridge
		Redleg partridge *
		Red grouse
		Blackgame
		Capercaillie
		Snipe
II Agricultural Pest Species		
Woodpigeon		Brown rat
Rabbit		
Grey Squirrel		
III Small Game Predators		
Polecat	Hedgehog	Weasel
Mink	Stoat	
Fox	Wildcat	
Magpie	Rook	
Hooded crow	Jackdaw	
Carrion crow	Jay	
*Excluding the contribution of hand-reared birds		

part of the overall prey population, which also includes small mammals and songbirds as well as agricultural pests like rabbits, and even the hand-reared pheasants and redleg partridges. Thus total prey abundance, including all these other items, might have increased, not declined. Third, other factors, such as agricultural intensification in the lowlands and overgrazing and commercial forestry in the uplands have had a direct and adverse effect, as well as the indirect effect of reducing the effectiveness of any predation control that a gamekeeper does.

Where detailed ecological studies have been undertaken there is now evidence that in many cases, common generalist predators like foxes and crows are indeed limiting numbers of small game in the uplands and lowlands—see Reynolds, Angelstam & Redpath (1988) for a review. This implies that in most cases a reduction in predation pressure is an essential part of any game recovery programme.

Does this mean we have return to the Edwardian style of management that was so clearly effective? Certainly not. A few perhaps would love to turn the clock back to such glorious times, but if this were to happen, the public reaction would be swift and final. Tenant farmers would resent their wishes being pushed aside in the drive to increase game stocks; conservationists would find a renewed persecution of predators unacceptable; and those concerned about animal rights would be shocked at the scale of the daily slaughter. In fact, most now agree that the Edwardian way of doing things was wrong. The idea of treating all predators as vermin, and

good for nothing but extermination, is unacceptable. The hen harrier and pine marten are again part of the upland scene as much as the blackcock and the red grouse. In the lowlands foxes and stoats are still part of the farmland community and few would wish it otherwise. Nevertheless, it is apparent that if the management of wild game for shooting is to continue, then the problem of the burgeoning populations of some of the more common predators needs to be addressed. To do this we need to have an ecologically sound philosophy within which to work. Fortunately 50 years of ecological research has provided us with the knowledge to frame such a philosophy.

Finding a Future for Game

We may dismiss Victorian and Edwardian game shooting as excessive, and we may even be appalled at the characters and practises of that era, but we should guard against labelling it as animal exploitation of the worst kind. For although it was done for pleasure rather than need, it had a significant redeeming quality not found very often in modern times. It was sustainable. Game populations were raised not lowered, and habitats were improved not depleted.

Exploitation is the unregulated and unmanaged use of natural resources, and 19th and early 20th century game management was not exploitation. Like Victorian farming it was a system based on managing animals and their habitats, largely without pesticides, artificial fertilisers or fossil fuels. In over half a century of game research, even though we understand significantly more biology and ecology than they did, we have not been able to improve on the results achieved by estate owners at the turn of the century.

Historically, we can think of wildlife management as going through at least four levels of development:

I. Subsistence Exploitation

By subsistence exploitation we mean hunting for food; primarily for the immediate and local needs of the family or group. Where practised by primitive cultures, this form of wildlife use is the most ancient and most natural. Normally, in stable environments, native peoples appear to have only a small impact on wildlife populations, usually for two main reasons: First, the human population is low and is itself limited by natural factors, particularly food resources. Second, animals are taken for local needs only. It is a common view today that this form of animal use is acceptable, whereas more developed "western" methods of wildlife use are seen as inevitably damaging and environmentally unsound. We tend to regard the various cultures of the North American Indian, the Australian Aborigine and the African Bushman as being harmonious hunting/gathering societies ecologically in balance with their habitat and their prey; a pristine natural existence we have now lost. However, it was not always so and the fossil and archaeological record suggests that this view is naive, at least in regard to the outset of these cultures. The real truth may be a frighteningly familiar tale of destruction.

Man is essentially a product of the Pleistocene epoch—the period of the ice ages, which started between one to two million years ago, although his roots in Africa are older. During and since that time he spread out of Africa into Europe, across Asia, into Australia (perhaps 50,000 years ago), and finally into the Americas via the Bering Straits at times when sea levels were low, most recently about 10 to 15,000 years ago. Thus by about 9000 years ago he had a global distribution. In historic times he has filled in, by learning to navigate, crossing to Madagascar, New Zealand, and oceanic islands.

The Pleistocene epoch was also a period when large mammals, a so called megafauna, were abundant over much of the globe. However, this megafauna suffered waves of extinction in each continent and there is evidence that these waves of annihilation were correlated with the arrival of man and his hunting technology (Martin, 1967). The American faunal extinction is particularly marked, with the rapid disappearance of mammoths, mastodons, horses, tapirs, camels, ground sloths and giant beavers more or less coincident with the appearance of the Paleo-Indians. The early Clovis point-making people killed large mammoths and mastodons, while the later Folsom point hunters took *Bison*

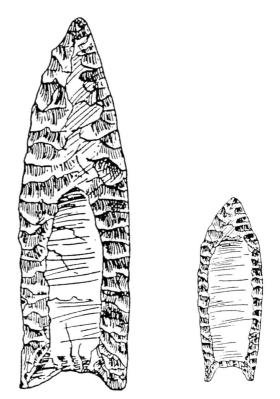

Paleo-Indian points. Left; a Clovis spear point probably for mastodon and mammoth and right a Folsom point used for bison. About actual size. (From, Bryan , 1967).

antiqus—a species later to become extinct as well. It seems as though early man was as deadly then as his counterpart is to day. More recently the extinction of the giant flightless moas in New Zealand coincided with the arrival of the Polynesian tribes, and even on the far flung oceanic islands like Hawaii, extinction of many flightless and large birds followed the arrival of the Polynesians (Diamond, 1991).

We know that introducing alien predators to a naive fauna can be catastrophic. For example, the accidental introduction of rats and deliberate release of stoats into New Zealand has put the survival of many of the native flightless birds in jeopardy (King, 1984). Pre-historic man was perhaps just like one of these alien predators when he arrived in new continents and was just as devastating as he has been in recent times.

II Commercial Exploitation

Natural subsistence exploitation took a more sinister turn when man became urbanised and developed trade routes. As his own population was no longer limited by the local habitat, his potential to damage wildlife resources increased. Trading allowed him access to remote and distant regions where he could carelessly deplete animal populations, often to near extinction.

Again, the history of the New World is littered with examples of over-exploitation for commercial gain. Fur, rather than gold, was the rich vein of untapped wealth which most early explorers reported back to their European sponsors. Some species like the sea otter, the northern fur seal, and the Antarctic fur seal were simply plundered as fast as they could be killed, skinned and shipped out. The result for such slow breeding species was a headlong decline in numbers and contraction in distribution. The Pribilof Island fur seals in the northern Pacific numbered between 1.5 and 2 million animals in the early 19th century but were reduced to only 200,000 by 1909 (Roppel & Davey, 1965). The Antarctic fur seal on South Georgia suffered a similar fate, with British and American sealers taking over 100,000 skins a year in the early 1800's, depleting stocks until there were none left a hundred years later. Happily, with 20th century protection and regulated harvesting, the numbers of both species have substantially recovered.

In the American continental interior the exploitation was slower and more methodical as the animals were dispersed, difficult to trap, and often found in remote regions with a harsh climate. Nevertheless, some highly valued species, like the beaver, were rapidly depleted and populations vanished progressively as the trappers moved further into the wilderness.

For other more robust species a sustained harvest was achieved which has allowed furs to be traded from the 17th century to the present day. The vast interior of the continent was explored in the 17th and 18th centuries by men like Henry Kelsey (1690) and Anthony Henday (1754), who were sponsored by the fur companies. By the end of the 18th century the Hudson's Bay Company had set up a network of trading stations throughout northern Canada, with furs being moved by boat down the large north flowing rivers into Hudson Bay, whence they were shipped to Europe each summer. Later, after bitter competition, they took over the trade of the North West Company, an originally French enterprise which had traded from the American mid-west and upper Mississippi regions, through the Great Lakes and St Lawrence River, to Europe. The Hudson's Bay Company thus established a complete fur

monopoly and a rule of law which extended over virtually the whole of Canada. This allowed them to trade huge quantities of fur involving a range of species, including beaver, muskrat, mink, marten, fisher, otter, lynx, Arctic fox and red fox. For most of these species they were able to sustain a commercial harvest for well over a hundred years without any form of wildlife management other than barter with native trappers. Their activity thus represents a rare example of unregulated commercial exploitation sustained over a long period and a wide area. In the process it has also provided population biologists with their longest ever series of wildlife data, and the fur returns for Lynx for the Mackenzie River district between 1821 and 1934 are the best example of population cycles we have yet found (Finerty, 1980; Elton & Nicholson, 1942).

III Regulated Hunting

For much of the 20th century man has attempted to regulate the harvesting of wildlife to prevent over-exploitation. A key principle behind regulated hunting is that wild populations are normally robust and to a large extent can compensate for losses due to hunting. This happens in two ways: First, hunting simply substitutes for other mortalities that the population normally sustains. For example, as a consequence of hunting, fewer may die of disease or get eaten by predators. Second, prey populations may breed faster and survive better when their numbers are lower. Therefore by regulating the number of game killed one can "harvest" a population at the same time as conserving its breeding stock.

It is ironic that many of the species which were decimated by commercial over-exploitation are in fact easy to manage by regulating the harvest. A classic example where conservation and regulated commercial hunting have brought about a remarkable recovery is case of the northern fur seal already referred to above.

The bulk of the population breeds on the Pribilof Islands of St Paul and St George. After the disastrous free-for-all in the 19th century, during which time the population was decimated twice, firstly by killing seals at the breeding grounds and secondly by killing them at sea after the rookeries were protected, the United States, Japan and Russia signed a treaty in 1911 to manage the stock. Initially no seals were killed, but later a harvest of male seals was taken each year based on the premise that since fur seals are polygamous the number of males could be reduced without reducing breeding potential. Fig 31.3 that shows this has been a major success, with the population increasing by about ten fold to the middle of this century (Roppel & Davey, 1965; Smith & Polacheck, 1981).

Animals generally produce more young and survive better when their densities are low. It follows that reducing the population increases potential harvesting rates, but a point will be reached where production is impaired because the breeding stock is too low. Fig 31.4 illustrates two theoretical curves which show how a "maximum sustainable yield" can be worked out for a species. In this example, shooting 20% of the pheasants every year will give an annual bag of about 400 birds, shooting 45% every year will increase the bag to almost 700 annually. However, if one where to kill 80% annually, the yield would be only some 300 birds—clearly "over-harvesting". As a general rule, in order to obtain a maximum or optimum sustainable yield, it is usually desirable to lower the population to allow the breeding performance to improve. In our example of the Pribilof Island fur seals, it was for this reason that the herd was deliberately reduced in the late 1950's and 1960's (Fig 31.3).

Almost as important as how many you can kill, is the question of when you kill them. You can obviously take many more if you harvest a species in the autumn, when numbers are at a peak and before any major winter mor-

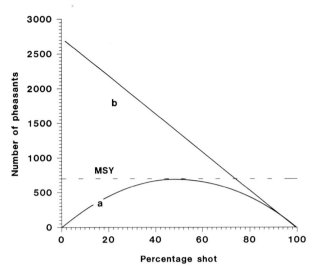

Fig 31.4 This graph shows harvesting rates for pheasants in relation to the game stock and the bag. The bottom axis is the percentage shot and left axis the number of birds either in the bag (a) or alive (b). The dome shaped curve shows how increasing the proportion shot increases the bag until the species is over-harvested and the bag declines. The sloping line is the total size of the population, which reduces with increasing harvest rates. The Maximum Sustainable Yield (MSY) for this population is therefore about 50% and this results in a maintained population of about 1500 birds. (After Robertson & Rosenberg, 1988).

tality, than if you wait till spring when numbers are minimum and when most animals start to breed. Thus the idea of a closed season is a very old one and goes back at least to Tudor times (Leopold, 1933). Equally old is the idea that females should be protected and only the males hunted—again helping productivity.

The key to regulating the harvest of game is therefore knowledge of the population dynamics of each species. Much game research around the world is thus directed towards this end. In management terms culling rates have to be carefully worked out in relation to annual censuses and variations in breeding success. Indeed the bulk of North American game management is directed to this course of action, and the techniques of the wildlife biologist are aimed at helping the authorities to obtain the best data for this kind of regulatory approach (e.g. Giles, 1971).

IV Wild Game Management

A natural extension of the idea that one can improve the harvest of game by regulating the level of hunting, is the concept that by careful management the productivity of game populations can be further increased. One might suspect that this requires a thorough understanding of the species before it is possible; however this does not need to be a scientific understanding—it can be an empirical one. In Britain this kind of knowledge was responsible for the high level of management that was achieved for species like the red grouse and

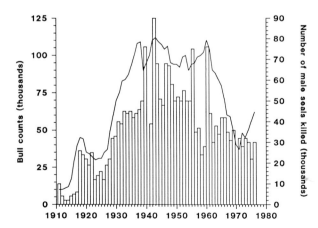

Fig 31.3 Fur seals on St. Paul Island. Line shows the population of breeding bull seals and the bars indicate the number of males culled. Females and non-breeding males are not shown. (After Smith & Polacheck, 1981)

the grey partridge during the late 19th and 20th centuries and which we have illustrated in this book. In the main this management has involved three factors; (1) improving of the habitat, (2) increasing the food supply and (3) reducing the effects of predation by removing predators. Although we could take examples of this approach from many parts of the world, this kind of management was pioneered on the British country estates. However, paradoxically the first leading advocate of this approach was an American, Aldo Leopold; although in fact his ideas derived from earlier sport hunters and naturalists (Reiger, 1986). Leopold realised that for many game species mere regulations were not enough and habitats had to be retained and created if game was to coexist with man in the New World (Leopold, 1933).

The net effect of these combined management techniques is that game stocks are substantially increased to a level which not only allows shooting but also means that even after shooting higher numbers of birds are maintained overall. This is shown graphically in Fig 31.5, which is based on our knowledge of the grey partridge (after Potts, 1984). This shows that increasing levels of management allow a high level of shooting which would not be sustainable otherwise. It also illustrates another paradox; that shooting and management often result in more birds than if they were protected from shooting and left unmanaged.

Leopold was somewhat cautious when it came to predator control, partly because he realised it could not be reduced to the simple axiom that anything that killed a game animal should be destroyed, and partly because in the American context he thought it was usually inappropriate. There is no doubt that predator control is one of the most controversial areas of game management and the idea that one should kill members of one species in order to enhance the numbers of another is anathema to some. In the British context, predator control has to be seen in relation to the total management package. Without it other management improvements would not be worthwhile. For example, improving the available nesting cover for grey partridge would result in only a small increase in numbers simply because predation losses would prevent the increased stock from breeding. In other words, predation is the primary limiting factor. Potts (1980) has illustrated this with a simulation model (Fig 31.6) which shows that with predator control, improving habitat very quickly results in an increased autumn stock; without control there is little effect. Many people believe that habitat creation is better for game than predator control. In a very real sense the opposite is true. Habitat improvement cannot be justified economically without it.

Although we have ranked these four stages in wildlife management, we do not wish to imply necessarily that

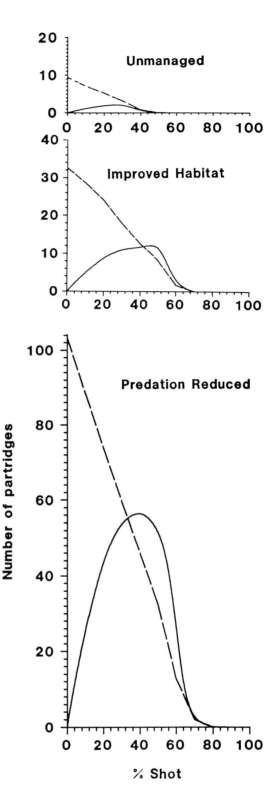

Fig 31.5 The effects of different levels of management on the harvesting rates and spring breeding stocks of grey partridge. Solid line represents size of the bag and dashed is the level of spring stock With no additional management spring stocks are very low and only very low levels of shooting are possible (top graph). Reducing the use of pesticides and improving the hedgerow cover increases the stock and the possible level of shooting (middle graph). At peak management with predation control as well (bottom graph) a maximum sustained yield can be obtained by shooting about 40% of the autumn stock. Note that even with a maximum sustained level of shooting, a highly managed population maintains a much higher breeding stock of birds than one that is unshot and unmanaged. After Aebischer (1991).

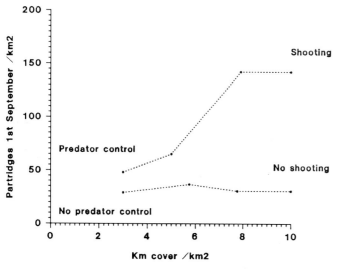

Fig 31.6 With predator control, increasing the amount of nesting cover results in a substantial increase in autumn stock—allowing shooting. With no predator control, improving the habitat does not result in more birds and shooting is not possible. Adapted from Potts (1980).

level IV is a kind of optimum. Actually, a level of wildlife management which may be appropriate in one ecosystem may be inappropriate in another. In near pristine environments with low numbers of indigenous people, continued subsistence hunting is often best preserved, since it not only helps the people to maintain their cultural identity and makes them less dependant on imported goods, but it also gives them a stake in preserving the system as a whole. Even where western urbanised man is the hunter, minimal management may be desirable. Many sport hunting areas in North America are state or province owned, and consist of natural or near natural habitats. In these situations high profile game management would conflict with a significant aspect of the sport, which is stalking a wild animal in an area that appears unmanaged and has a semblance of wilderness. In Britain our countryside is man-made and supports a high level of human activity. Thus a high degree of management is desirable, otherwise many game species would dwindle to extinction even if given legal protection.

A crucial element of this management is the reduction of predation by controlling predators. As we have seen this has, in the past, led to the near extinction of some predatory birds and mammals, so understandably it is opposed by many interested in conservation but with little knowledge of shooting and game management. This therefore is a pivotal issue upon which the future of wild game management depends.

Predator Control or Predation Control

Attitudes to predators have gone through a huge cycle of change during the last century. When our Victorian and Edwardian forefathers were protecting their game they were uncompromising about eliminating any potential enemy. In Norfolk for example, a fox or a stoat

seen on the estate was a serious matter and it was hunted down until it had been destroyed. They were referred to as vermin and treated in much the same way as we might today treat rats living under the garden shed or compost heap. Such attitudes were the society norm and extended throughout our western culture. In North America, when all hunting and trapping was banned within the boundaries of Yellowstone National Park in 1894, wolves were made an exception and their persecution continued.

If our change in attitudes to predators in Britain and Europe has been through a cycle of change, in America the turning tide of opinion has been like a flood. The history of American predator control is an extreme example. Dunlap (1988) documents how in western states wolves, coyotes and other large predators like bears and cougars were regarded not only as enemies of deer and elk, but more importantly of cattle and sheep. By the 1920's such a head of steam had built up against predators that the Federal government was forced to create the Division of Predator and Rodent Control (PARC) whose main policy was to eliminate these predators from western states. Agents of the division (nick-named the "gopher-chokers" for their other role in dealing with prairie dogs and ground squirrels) began systematic poisoning campaigns using cyanide and the new compound "1080" to which wolves and coyotes were particularly susceptible. By 1950 virtually all the western ranching states were saturated with poison bait stations. However, successful though these policies were in terms of reducing losses to predators, the public outcry was becoming intense and PARC was under severe pressure by the 1960's. It was not until 1972 that "1080" and other poisons were banned for predator control. Now, just two decades later, the wolf—like the bald eagle—has come to symbolise wildlife conservation and efforts are being made to reintroduce it to its former range.

As biologists we are caught on the horns of a dilemma. On the one hand we know that predation has a big impact on game stocks, and on the other as conservationists we want to conserve the very animals that are causing the damage. Can there be a way out? Apart from giving up one or the other, our only hope is to try to reduce the problem to the essentials and to be discriminating in our approach. First, we need to be clear about the objectives. From the game point of view the object is to reduce predation—it is not to control predator numbers. So, we should not be aiming to reduce numbers of foxes, but to reduce the damage they do. For example, for grey partridge the key time when predation is significant is during the two month nesting season, when eggs can be stolen by crows and hen birds killed by foxes. At other times of the year the risk of predation is lower and the population consequences less. Thus the period when predators need to be killed

can be reduced to a short window of time. Since, in England gamekeepered areas now represent only scattered patches of countryside, this short-term control will only have a very limited impact on the status of the predator species as a whole. This kind of approach clearly needs to be adopted more widely but we also need to explore other means of reducing predation, such as better designed habitats, and providing alternative food for predators during vulnerable periods. Ultimately however, we probably have to compromise and settle for moderate and selective amounts of predator reduction and the moderate game bags that go with it. Part of the challenge for the future will be to ensure that such moderation is also economically the most feasible and socially the most desirable option.

In controlling predation to benefit game, we must not forget that predators have a value beyond their intrinsic beauty, and they may play a far wider role in ecosystems than we perhaps realise. Only when we remove them do we understand how deep these interactions can be. There is no more remarkable example than the case of Pacific sea otter (Reidman & Estes, 1990; Estes, Rathbun & Van Blaricom, in press). This delightful creature, which floats on its back knocking open clam shells on its tummy, and munching sea urchins in the way we might eat an apple, represents one of the success stories of modern conservation. With a former distribution around the whole of the northern Pacific rim, it was progressively exterminated by the fur hunters

of the 18th and 19th centuries until it was protected by an international treaty in 1911. Since then the remaining colonies have expanded and new ones been started by reintroductions or natural colonisation. In the meantime, in the absence of otters, significant human fisheries based on clams and abalone shellfish had developed. With the reappearance of the sea otter it had been supposed that man and otter could coexist, with the fishermen taking a smaller but sustainable harvest. In fact they couldn't, and one by one the fisheries collapsed as the sea otters champed their way through the beds of shellfish. With time the otters themselves ran short of clams and fed more heavily on sea urchins, of which there was an abundance. As the otters reduced the grazing urchins along the rocky California coast they allowed the natural seaweeds to re-establish where they had been absent for well over 100 years. Now in these areas the giant kelp forest ecosystem is once again reappearing in places where it had long been lost. It is as if this otter is more than just another carnivore, it is the key to the survival of a whole ecosystem. Indeed it is referred to as a "keystone" species (Reidman & Estes, 1990).

The lesson from the sea otter is that even in our man-made landscape of rural England, ecosystems need predators *and* their prey. If we manage our wild game for shooting, we certainly need to reduce predation and usually this means killing predators. However, paradoxically we need to conserve them as well (Morrison,

1989). Thus in the future we shall have to manage both predators and game, and move away from the dichotomy of protection or persecution which has characterised much of our approach until now.

A key player in this future scenario has to be the gamekeeper. For too long his role in the countryside has been underrated. Too often he is treated at best as a quaint country anachronism, or at worst a cruel ignoramus who will kill anything that so much as looks at a pheasant. He is frequently blamed for disregarding the law, persecuting protected species, and using illegal methods. There is no question that this has indeed happened, but gamekeepers are not natural criminals and we should try to understand why this has occurred. In most cases it is because the tools of their trade have been proscribed, and yet their future employment is put in jeopardy if they fail to produce enough game to shoot. The solution is to elevate the gamekeeper's role in the countryside, not to diminish it.

In the future the gamekeeper needs to be better paid, better trained, and better represented. We must ensure that he has the means at his disposal to protect the game he produces, and we must listen to his problems and resolve them speedily. In return we must expect him to stick to the letter of the law, and take on the role of a countryside warden, able to explain to the public the benefits of his work, as well as supervising the increased levels of access that society demands.

Squaring Conservation with Game Management

An all embracing kind of game management which includes not only the game and their habitats, but their predators as well, offers us a way of conserving much of our landscape in a form which is not simply a relict of some former era but is a productive and attractive part of a diverse rural economy.

In Britain, the origins of conservation stretch back through the centuries, beginning with the royal forests and chases preserved for hunting. However, in North America this same process has been telescoped and we can see quite clearly how game preservation and game management laid the foundations for the wider conservation and environmental movement we see today. These origins can be traced to the early sport hunters in the 1870's, who deplored the "commercial gunning" that wiped out the buffalo herds and the passenger pigeon. They tried to instil a sportsman-like attitude towards hunting, along the lines of what they had seen in Europe but set in the pioneer context of the North American wilderness. This new conservation ethic was expounded by hunters in magazines like *Forest and Stream* and by societies like the Boone and Crockett Club. Its founding father was George Bird Grinnell who edited *Forest and Stream*, founded the Audubon Society, and campaigned tirelessly for a hunter-conservation ethic. He persuaded others like Theodore Roosevelt to take up these issues at the highest level and get public support for institutions like the National Parks.

Much later, it was Aldo Leopold who, better than anybody else, was able to define the link between hunting and conservation. He eloquently expressed the emotional response of the hunter which transcends the mere killing of game. As a hunter and an ecologist he was able to impart a deep, almost philosophical, understanding of nature to his readers. In his book *"A Sand County Almanac"* (Leopold, 1949) this mix of emotion and ecological perceptiveness shines through most clearly. In the final chapters of this book he pleads for a "Land Ethic" which he hopes farmers, foresters and game hunters will adopt. In a very real sense he was responding to the exploitation of the land in the same way as Grinnell had been responding to the exploitation of game half a century earlier. Leopold felt that government incentives given to farmers for conservation were not enough and it was necessary to instil in them a land ethic based on the "wise use" of natural resources, particularly the soil, but also the flora and fauna it supported. In 1948, within six months of writing this book, Leopold had died.

During the forty years since his death, in spite of ecology, conservation and the environment being high on the political agenda in Europe and North America, there has been little sign of such a land ethic developing. Indeed what we have been encouraging farmers and foresters to adopt is a "Commercial Ethic". The failure of the land ethic idea is that it often runs counter to profitability. A modern English arable farmer trying to adopt a traditional ley rotation, which builds on natural soil fertility, would find his profit margin evaporate and his bank balance spiralling into the red. But farming and forestry are subsidised industries. We need to switch the subsidies to support sustainability, so that profits depend more on maintaining the renewable productivity of the soil and less on the amount of industrial input in the forms of fertiliser and pesticide.

Small game animals are sensitive species, not just to predation, but to habitat and environmental quality as well. Grey partridge, brown hare, common snipe, red grouse, black grouse and capercaillie are amongst those suffering through over-specialised or over-intensive land use. More sustainable renewable agriculture in the uplands and lowlands would benefit game enormously, and coupled with a reduction in predation most of the species we have seen decline would recover quite quickly. Their breeding potential is, after all, very high. With sustainable land use, game management could rightly take its place in a system integrated with farming, forestry, and recreation, to increase overall countryside revenues. This would do more to encourage Leopold's land ethic than any amount of sermonising.

Some people think we should leave wildlife to the balance of nature. They lack a sense of history. Leopold put it well.....

"There are those who shy at the prospect of a man-made game crop as something artificial and therefore repugnant. This attitude shows good taste but poor insight. Every head of wild life still alive in this country is already artifi-cialized, in that its existence is conditioned by economic forces. Game management merely proposes that their impact shall not remain merely fortuitous. The hope for the future lies not in curbing the influence of human occupancy—it is already too late for that—but in creating a better understanding of the extent of that influence and a new ethic for its governance."

From: "Game Management", Aldo Leopold (1933)

The future of game, and the many species of plant and animal which share their habitats and environmental needs, depends on the farmers and landowners. It is they who, whether we like it or not, are custodians of our countryside. Ironically one of the biggest dangers facing our game species is over-protection. Unless sportsmen can shoot the game they cherish, they will lack the motivation to conserve and manage them and the landscape in which they are nurtured. They will lose heart; turning away from wild game management and instead towards plans for a new golf course, a housing estate, or a theme park on their rural acres. Man is *part* of the ecosystem—he always has been.

APPENDICES

APPENDIX I

THE GAME CONSERVANCY'S
NATIONAL GAMEBAG CENSUS

Early Uses of Bag-records

Gamebag records were recognised as useful population indicators by biologists more than a century ago. Alfred Newton, Professor of Zoology at the University of Cambridge wrote the following in 1861:

> *" I allude to the "Game books" which are now so commonly kept on different manors; and I think that nothing but a little ordinary care in applying the results to be obtained from a somewhat general inspection of these useful registers would furnish a sufficiently accurate return as far as relates to the Grey Partridge. No doubt many proprietors might evince a disinclination to submit such valuable records to be examined by a stranger; but much of this might also be overcome by the tact of the ornithological statistician who could with good reason urge that, by the comparison of local registers of this description, he would from them very possibly supply preservers of game with many deductions of a highly important nature. For from an extended examination of such books, or abstracts of such books, it is not unreasonable to suppose that he would be enabled to tender many recommendations worthy of attention."*

Clearly such records were at their most useful when comparing game management from one estate to the next. Perhaps the first systematic use in this way was by Lord Lovat (1911) in relation to the management of red grouse. Analysing bag-records and taking 5 and 10 year averages enabled his committee not only to compare the performance of one moor with another but to assess the implementation of management practises such as heather burning. He was also able to examine the reasons behind the recurrence of population crashes or outbreaks of grouse disease, which were having such an economic impact in the uplands.

The first pioneering scientific studies of the ecology of animal populations were started at the University of Oxford in the 1920's and 1930's by Charles Elton. He realised at once the value of long-term data, and the Bureau of Animal Population he set up at Oxford drew extensively on wildlife records of all sorts. The most famous to be unearthed at this time were the fur-trading records of the Hudson's Bay Company in Northern Canada. These revealed the classic ten year Snowshoe hare and Canadian lynx cycle which has become almost a cliché in the teaching of wildlife biology. Less well known were the data from other sources, and in particular the game shooting records from British sporting estates. Although these originated from an area a fraction the size of the Canadian sample, the records were far more difficult to analyse. First, they were from a highly heterogeneous managed landscape, and more importantly the shooting and the recording was done under the regime of a changing progression of a landowners with different talents and interests, rather than the unswerving rule of a British imperial trading company. Nevertheless, an attempt at a serious analysis was made. Elton employed the services of a young biologist, Douglas Middleton, to carry out an investigation of cycles from data in estate game books. In the then infant *Journal of Ecology*, Middleton published a paper showing how bag-records from game books fluctuated from year to year, and he interpreted many of these as cycles of varying lengths (Middleton, 1934).

Later Middleton organised a wide ranging survey of British sporting estates, soliciting game records and details of areas and habitats on the shoots. He was helped in the task by Helen Chitty, wife of the later well known Canadian population biologist Dennis Chitty. A large number of questionnaires were sent out and returned with varying amounts of information. If bag records were kept in game books, owners were asked to give details of the major quarry species, particularly for the periods 1888 to 1897 and 1928 to 1937. However, a form was provided to cover numbers of game shot since 1860. Many estates filled in as much as was possible from their game books. The intention of the survey was to compare game abundance in the era after World War I compared to the perceived optimum around the turn of the century. Records were gathered throughout 1938 and organised in separate files by estate. A preliminary tally of the numbers of partridge shot per thousand acres of farmland was made for each place. However this was as far as the analysis proceeded before the second war intervened and biologists at the Bureau were assigned to work on species such as rats and rabbits, which were having a serious effect on food production.

Most of this early game research was funded by the cartridge manufacturing business of Eley Bros., a subsidiary of ICI which had established a virtual monopoly on the sale of shotgun cartridges in Britain. In 1933 Major H.G. Eley, inheritor of the family business, set up a game research centre at Knebworth in Hertfordshire. In 1946 the station was moved to Fordingbridge in Hampshire, and after Eley's retirement in 1952, Middleton was appointed Manager. ICI's involvement in game research was pecuniary rather than philanthropic and their objective was to increase cartridge sales substantially by reviving game shooting, which had more or less collapsed with the outbreak of war. The research at Fordingbridge between 1949 and 1959 was almost wholly based on an experimental partridge shoot at Damerham, where the emphasis was on demonstrating that wild partridge management was possible in the post-war environment and on trying to develop methods appropriate to the new era.

During this period ICI advisory staff were visiting estates and shoots across the country helping to get these ideas into practise. At the same time they were gathering game shooting and game density information from the places they were visiting, and by 1959 pheasant, partridge and woodpigeon bags were being collected from some 300 localities.

Following the myxomatosis epidemic in rabbits (1953/4), ICI discovered to its dismay that most of its cartridge sales were for rabbit rather than gamebird shooting, so they seriously questioned whether basic research was worthwhile at all. They were also discouraged by the fact that the ecologists at Fordingbridge were stressing the importance of summer weather to wild game production—something that even the mighty ICI could have little influence over. Consequently ICI decided to pull out of game research and from 1960 continued only to fund the advisory side as the Eley Game Advisory Station directed by Charles Coles. The research arm was cut adrift as the Game Research Association, with Middleton as Director, to be funded solely by private members' subscriptions.

Launching the Scheme

Led by Doug Middleton, the Game Research Association had an initial membership of 460 which increased to nearly 3000 by 1968. No longer with its own experimental shoot, the need to monitor trends in game abundance throughout Britain was much more keenly felt by research staff, particularly their ornithologist John Ash, and in 1961 a game census was formally set up by Ash and Middleton. This need was emphasised by the spreading environmental problems caused by the growth of agrochemical farming; particularly the organochlorine insecticides.

Burgate Manor, Fordingbridge. Headquarters of The Game Conservancy.

The game census contained three parts. First, a partridge survey based on a spring census of breeding pairs on each estate, followed by a sample young-to-old ratio count in autumn to calculate annual production. Second, a bag recording scheme; and third, something quite new, a pest and predator record. These last two parts are now referred to as the National Game Bag Census. The pest and predator record had grown from the knowledge that many efficient gamekeepers usually kept a note book or diary of their activities and these could provide a useful guide not only as to the efficiency of predator control, but also an insight into to the changing abundance of predators. Instead of a one off survey like the Bureau of Animal Population had conducted, the game census would obtain annual information so that game stocks and the game harvest could be monitored from year to year. Subscribers of bag records were sent a questionnaire at the end of each season asking for details of the bag and any birds reared. Those who wished to submit details of vermin were sent an additional form to cover a range of the significant game predators and pest species. To encourage good record keeping subscribers were also offered nicely printed record forms on good quality paper which could be kept in their own ring files or later bound as a game book. In 1961 some 450 subscribers sent in their bag records and the Game Research Association began to publish results for pheasant and partridge on an annual basis in its reports. Average bags were calculated regionally and the regions used at this time (Fig 32.1) reflected very much the distribution of contributors rather than natural geographic zones or equal sized parts of Britain.

Year by year as the data built up, the difficulty of analysing species other than partridge and pheasant became increasingly formidable; it had to be done by hand. Furthermore, even for these species, with a system based on census forms and a card index of contributors it was well nigh impossible to use a proper statistical analysis on the data. Consequently the routine was to summarise the information by adding up the total bag for each species in each region and dividing by the total acreage of those supplying data. Such an average was of course weighted by estate size but more seriously the method provided no way of calculating standard errors to judge the significance of regional or annual differences.

By 1968 the Game Research Association was in financial difficulties, and at the same time its research performance was heavily criticised by outside scientific advisers. These conditions, and ICI's continued reduction in funding of the Eley Game Advisory Station, brought the two organisations together again under the new banner of The Game Conservancy. There was a substantial increase in membership fees and charges for advisory work were introduced. The new organisation was directed by Charles Coles and responsibility for research was given to Terence Blank, a biologist who had remained with the Eley Game Advisory Station and been involved with the partridge research at Damerham since the late 1940's. The game census was maintained by Blank throughout the late sixties and early 1970's, but the problem of analysing the accumulating data was not seriously tackled. Furthermore, many contributors lapsed, partly because some Game Research Association members had declined to join The Game Conservancy at the higher subscription rate, and possibly also because of the limited feedback of results in Game Conservancy publications. In 1976 with Blank's retirement, research was put under the direction of Dick Potts. Potts, a former sea-bird ecologist from Durham University, had originally been employed by the Game Research Association to try to find the causes for the post-war collapse of grey partridge populations. He had been running a small team of scientists in Sussex on an extensive study area covering over 12 miles of chalk arable land. Examining the bag records from farms on this area, and elsewhere, had showed him that it was not just partridge abundance that had changed. Other species like hares, rabbits, stoats and jackdaws also showed significant population trends. So in 1976 when he moved to Fordingbridge he gave the rehabilitation and modernisation of the National Game Bag Census a high priority. This task was undertaken by the author, a former member of the partridge team who had been trying to assess the impact of weasels and stoats on the survival of partridge chicks.

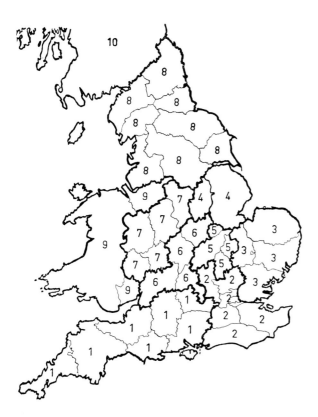

Fig 32.1 Regions used in the game census between 1961 and 1977.

Restructuring for Computer

The main problem of modernisation was to implement a cost-effective system which would store the data and allow trends and other statistics to be calculated by machine. Microprocessors had not been invented and even the new electronic calculators were only just beginning to offer statistical functions. In 1977 The Game Conservancy's Council was persuaded to buy a small minicomputer.

To implement a computer run database it is essential to start with a logically organised set of records. In its original form The National Game Bag Census had a card index which held the names and addresses of subscribers divided by counties; the annual returns being grouped by year and region. Since there was no coding system and because estate names, owners and acreages could change over the years, keeping track of the source of data was becoming difficult. Already staff were using such methods as comparing handwriting to identify returns when information was incomplete! The running of the scheme then had to be redesigned.

Fig 32.3 Distribution of contributors to the National Game Bag Census in 1977.

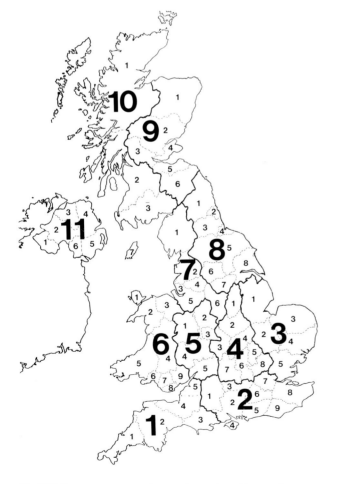

Fig 32.2 Game census region and county system set up in 1977 and now used for all data, past and present.

The first step was a more sensible regional breakdown, with approximately similar sized regions built up using the new administrative county boundaries. Each place was assigned a unique five figure code; the first two digits defined one of 10 possible regions, the third digit the county within that region, and the last two the estate number within a county (Fig 32.2). The idea behind this system was that even though for most analyses species would need to be looked at by region and year, one could also easily select records from groups of regions or counties by specifying upper and lower limits to a range of code numbers. It also allowed data from individual estates to be picked out as well. Grid references were included for plotting purposes and because it was sometimes becoming quite difficult to trace the continuity through a series of records when estates changed hands, split up or altered their names. All contributors were circulated with a questionnaire to obtain these grid references.

By spring 1978 the new computer based system was running and a new annual form was sent to contributors. This included a wider range of species and the pest and predator details as well. The pest and predator section could be left blank if these records were not available.

Recent Additions

A serious deficiency in the National Game Bag Census from the outset had been the dearth of records relating to red grouse and upland shooting (Fig 32.3). The origins of this stem from decisions taken in the 1960's not to undertake grouse research but to leave that to the Nature Conservancy team (now the Institute of Terrestrial Ecology) at Banchory. It was not until 1979 that The Game Conservancy began detailed ecological studies of red grouse. The impetus came from moor owners in the north of England, principally The Earl Peel at Gunnerside, who felt that a project should investigate practical solutions to moorland problems and which would complement the fundamental studies being done at Banchory. Grouse populations in England were actually doing rather well during this era, but they had the recurrent problem of repeated crashes in stock which made planning the shooting season difficult and seriously influenced the economics of grouse moor management. These population crashes were often such that on some Pennine moors, years with several thousand grouse bagged were followed by years with only one or two hundred. Trying to find ways of reducing the extent of these crashes were fundamental, and The Game Conservancy's North of England Grouse research project began by examining them. To get data

Fig 32.4 Estates which provide bag records from grouse moors in the north of England.

on the frequency of these cycles, moor owners were circulated with a questionnaire asking for bag records from their moor. Using the computer, a complete time series analysis of these records was undertaken, clearly showing the quasi-cyclic nature of the Pennine grouse populations, fluctuating on average every 4.8 years. Over 50 series were examined, documenting for the first time the extent and nature of these cycles in the

north of England (Tapper, 1983; Potts, Tapper & Hudson, 1984). These grouse bag records immediately provided an injection of grouse data to the National Game Bag Census and all respondents to this survey were added to the mailing list (Fig 32.4).

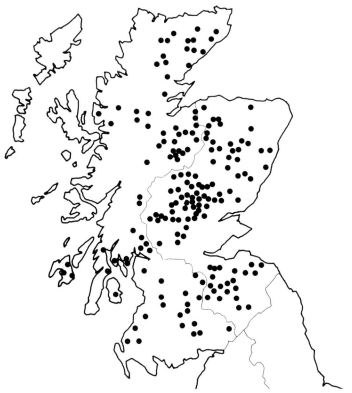

Fig 32.5 Location of grouse moors providing bag records to the Scottish grouse survey.

By 1984, The Game Conservancy, now under the direction of Richard Van Oss, was expanding, and a further project on red grouse in Scotland was needed. Here the problem was not fluctuating bags but a catastrophic decline that began in 1976 and by 1984 was showing no sign of bottoming out. Consequently our analysis of grouse bags in Scotland, based on a survey conducted by Richard Barnes, emphasised trend rather than cycles. Barnes managed to obtain bag records from 169 Scottish moors which probably represented about half of all active grouse moors north of the border. This research (Barnes, 1987) has provided the background to the recent Game Conservancy studies of red grouse in Scotland. Again, as in the North of England, the survey has broadened the base of National Game Bag Census.

These grouse surveys obtained historical bag records from game books (often well into the 19th century) so they could be used to revise estimates of grouse returns for years prior to the survey. With records on computer, updating files is a straightforward matter, and trends for some species could be calculated back well beyond 1961. However the grouse surveys only provided such long-term data for upland species. For the lowlands other sources of data were needed.

The first historical lowland data for the National Game Bag Census were obtained more by happy accident than by organised plan. During efforts to establish the credibility, particularly of the predator records, to justify the purchase of a computer in 1977, it was essential to show how proper standard errors should be calculated around each annual data point using unweighted means. The trends for rabbits and stoats in East Anglia were chosen as suitable examples. Using an early electronic calculator (without statistical functions or memory register) the task was begun and proceeded at the rate of about two points (years) per day. To relieve the monotony occasional diversions were needed and one such was to explore the contents of The Game Conservancy cellar. Mouldering pathological specimens, stuffed game birds, archaic traps, broken furniture and old papers were all mixed together and due for disposal. Under a heap of all this was a cardboard box, rotting at the bottom where the cellar had flooded. Untying the string revealed a large pile of files, and opening the uppermost showed.. "OXFORD UNIVERSITY: BUREAU OF ANIMAL POPULATION. GAME SURVEY". Thus after nearly 40 years, Middleton's original data was rediscovered.

After the purchase of a new microcomputer with a hard disk in 1983 this historical (pre-1961) information from both the uplands and the lowlands was added to the database. It turned out that many of the pre-war records could be linked to current contributors to the census and could be given the same code number. However, in the lowlands there were virtually no historical data from the period 1938-1961. In 1985, Mike Rands, a partridge ecologist who was helping to run the scheme at the time, sent out a general appeal to Game Conservancy members asking for records from game books. Those that replied were sent a questionnaire, this yielded records from another 62 estates.

In the future, more historical data will be added to the scheme as it becomes available, so all our analysis will be subject to constant revision. However, as sample sizes increase, the effect of these additions on the national figures for the main game species is likely to be minimal.

Analysis of the bag and associated predator records has followed two separate strands. First, annual results are calculated at the end of each shooting season to assess game production, and second various investigations are made of the changing status and trends in the bags of different species.

The results for key species have been published in reports of the Game Research Association and later The Game Conservancy. These have been primarily intended for the membership, both to sustain interest in the scheme and also to enable contributors to compare their own estate records with national figures. Initially, summary tables were prepared for each area for pheasant, partridge and mallard, as well as for seven predators; these can be found in the Game Research Association reports of the early 1960's. In later years just the pheasant and partridge figures were presented in early Game Conservancy reviews. After the 1977 reorganisation, data for grey partridge, redleg partridge, red grouse, brown hare, woodcock and woodpigeon were presented as regional maps, and subsequently either a map or a national trend has usually been presented annually for these species as well as the pheasant.

The second strand of results, looking particularly at trends in individual species, have usually first appeared as reports in Game Conservancy annual reviews and often led to papers in journals, books or symposia. These papers and reports however do not give an idea and flavour of the whole National Game Bag Census scheme, so the intention of this volume has been to present a broad analysis of all the main species in a way which allows cross species comparisons. Here we have been able to see these trends in the context of the changing countryside and alterations in game management.

I.C.I. Game Researches

APPENDIX II

CHANGES OVER TIME

As we have seen, the National Game Bag Census has gradually built up over the years partly by recruiting new subscribers but also through surveys asking land-owners to supply information from their gamebooks. Taken as a whole it is not surprising that the amount of data available in different decades varies considerably.

Fig 33.1 shows the changes in the total area of ground covered by the scheme. The peak year (1964) covered 1.5 million hectares (3.7 million acres). The grouse moor area now represents about half of the total National Game Bag Census area, and it peaked in 1983 at 730,000 hectares or 1.8 million acres. Because of the large changes in area in our sample since 1900 it is appropriate to express our data almost always as number killed per 100 hectares of total area. In most cases, woodland and grouse moor areas are also given, so it is also possible to calculate numbers on the basis of these two habitats, or combinations of them. For example, for a farmland species one might exclude the grouse moor area and express numbers shot per unit area of remaining ground. In practice however, this can lead to exaggerated bag densities because some typical farmland species such as brown hares and grey partridges are also shot on moorland fringes. So on shoots with some farmland and grouse moor, bag densities will be too high when calculated on the basis of the remaining farmland area only. A further point is that areas of different habitats tend to be recorded less accurately than the total area.

The main difference between the data used for long-term series and those in the post-war national trend, is that in the latter the sample size is consistently high (ie always greater than 500 estates in any year—Fig 33.2). However, the available data from the period 1900 to 1985 varies from as few as 143 up to a maximum of 703. Such a big variation would be bound to affect the trends in some way, so for this reason we adopted the strategy of taking a sub-sample of estates which had virtually complete sets of data back to the turn of the century.

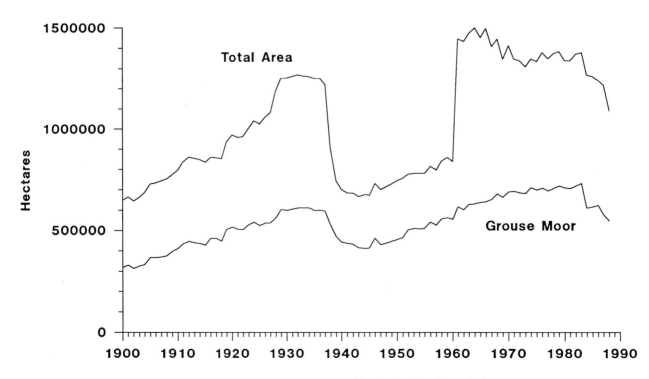

Fig 33.1 The total survey area and the area of grouse moor covered by all data in this analysis.

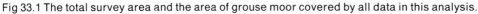

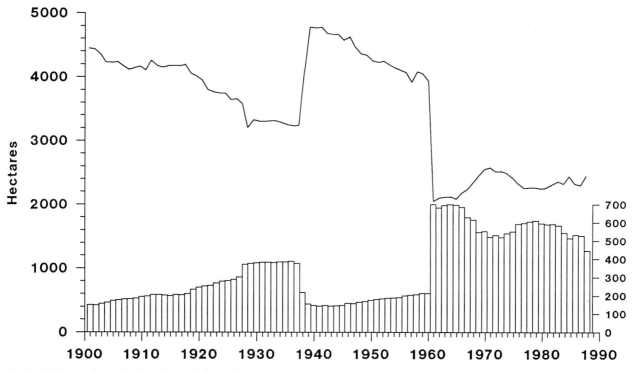

Fig 33.2 The number of estates for which we have data year by year since 1900 (bars—right axis), and the average area of these estates (line—left axis). There is a tendency for bigger estates to have longer-term records which were maintained through the war years.

Cycles—Time series analysis

One of the most interesting phenomena in ecology is the occurrence of cycles or rhythmic fluctuations in animal numbers over long periods of time. The study of cycles has been a recurrent theme of population biologists since Elton's classic work *"Voles, mice and lemmings"* (Elton, 1942). However, since the fluctuations in question are often up to 10 years in length, it is not easy to find data which spans periods of time long enough for a proper analysis. For game species however, we are fortunate in having long series of bag data on which this analysis can be done.

Before embarking on a description of how we have analysed these cycles it is important to be clear just what exactly it is we are looking for. Firstly we are not concerned with trend, but with the variation around it. This can be random or nearly so, or can fluctuate in an apparently cyclic way.

Nisbet & Gurney (1982) have classified the various patterns that animal populations might exhibit. These are:

1. True-cycles.

2. Phase-remembering quasi-cycles.

3. Phase-forgetting quasi-cycles.

4. Non-cyclic. Type (A) where the data are completely random, and type (B) where each point is partially affected by the previous year.

1. True-cycles

These are perfect cycles; in fact, sine waves. Like alternating current or light, the wavelength can vary, as can the amplitude, but they are mathematically precisely predictable without any error. In animal population terms however, such cycles are a kind of unachievable nirvana, useful only as a concept against which to compare our real population data.

2. Phase-remembering quasi-cycles

These are clearly cyclic populations, but which also include some random variation as well, so that peaks and troughs are sometimes of differing magnitude, and even the cycle length may alter slightly. However, they have no tendency to drift out of phase, so that a population peak in ten years time is statistically as easy to predict as one in a thousand years time. In other words the animal population is locked into a rhythm to which it returns after perturbation.

3. Phase-forgetting quasi-cycles

These are like the group above except here the cycles do drift out of phase, either slowly or rapidly. This means that the probability of accurately predicting a cycle diminishes with time. In fact change can be so rapid that even predicting the next maxima may be highly unreliable.

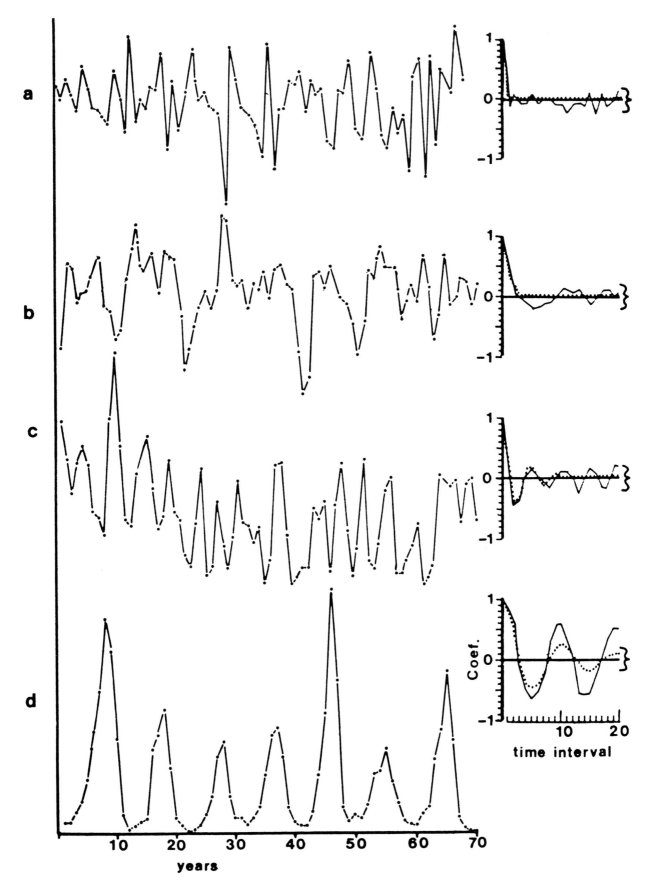

Fig 33.3 Four types of time series patterns and their correlograms. Top, a truly random series of type 4a; next, a random series but with some association between adjacent years—type 4b, next, phase forgetting quasi-cycles; and bottom, phase remembering quasi-cycles. The correlograms show values of the auto-correlation coefficients with a time interval up to 20 years. Notice that in the random series coefficients are always close to zero, except when association between adjacent years gives a significant positive value at an interval of one. The phase forgetting quasi-cyclic series show significant negative coefficients only at intervals of 2 and 3 years—the rest are damped to near zero. This suggests a cyclic period of about 5 years. For the phase remembering series the correlogram shows a sustained oscillation with a period of almost 10 years.

4. Non-cyclic populations

Populations that do not cycle but vary at random can do so in either of two ways. First, all the variation can be due to chance, through the control of random factors which influence the population. Such variation is purely haphazard and the population in any year has no relationship to the number in the previous or following years (type A). In the second (type B) there is some association with the previous year or several preceding years. This is usually because animal life spans extend over several years. So for example, a really good summer will not only increase production but also benefit the following years stock as well.

Time series analysis

The methods used to analyse and test for the presence of cycles are called time series analysis. They can be rather daunting mathematically and although such techniques as spectral analysis are very powerful tools in the interpretation of cycles, they are not always easy for the non specialist to understand. Thus we have chosen to employ here less elaborate methods. We make no apology to mathematicians who may regard our approach as out of date.

Our analysis (as does any time series analysis) depends on a simple statistical principle—that of the correlation coefficient. Thus the more two variables have similar pairs of values, ie are positively correlated, the closer this coefficient is to one. With no association at all coefficients are around zero, and negative coefficients occur when high values of one are paired with low values of the other and vice versa. For time series analysis, the two variables we are using are based on a single set of records in time sequence. Thus, this is often termed auto-correlation.

The pairs in the auto-correlation calculation are all values for years a given distance apart. Thus we start to calculate a correlation coefficient for all pairs of values just one year apart, then two years apart, then three and so on. Eventually we end up with a series of coefficients at increasing time intervals which we can plot as a graph—a correlogram. Examination of this correlogram indicates the cyclic nature or otherwise of the series.

Fig 33.3 shows examples of the four different types of time series we are likely to encounter in bag record data (2, 3, 4A & 4B above). Alongside each we show the calculated correlogram. Looking at our purely random series of type 4A, there is no association between pairs of years at any time interval. If a value happens to be high the adjacent year is just as likely to be low as it is high, similarly with other time intervals the likelihood

of it being similar to our chosen point is no greater than any other random value. Thus when we plot the correlogram for this series it will appear as a wiggly line around the zero coefficient base line with virtually no coefficients falling outside the + 0.2 to -0.2 region. In the random series of type 4b the coefficients at a time interval of one year are significantly positive (about + 0.5) for the reasons explained above.

For a cyclic series the correlogram will also show a cycle pattern. This is because where the time interval between our pair of points is a multiple of the cycle length the coefficient will be highly positive. Thus for a population that cycles every ten years (as type 2 in Fig 33.3) a comparison between points of 10, 20 or 30 years apart will always give a high coefficient irrespective of whether they are taken from the cyclical peak or any other phase. If we choose points 5, 15 or 25 years apart they will always be negatively related. So the correlogram appears as a cycle which does not damp down with time.

With phase forgetting quasi-cycles the correlogram does have a damped appearance. This is because with time, variations in cycle length cause the correlation coefficients to get weaker. So in the case of type 3 in Fig 33.3, a phase forgetting 5 year cycle, the negative coefficients at 2 and 3 years are marked but the rest are too weak to be significant.

This is the theory. How does it work in practice with real data? There are two essential differences between the kind of examples we have shown and the real series on which we want to work. First, time-series analysis can only be done on series that are trend-free, in other words that are not declining or increasing with time. Many of our bag data are doing just this, and so we need a method of getting rid of the trend before we start. Second, even though we have bag records for about hundred years in some cases, these are still rather short runs of data for this kind of mathematics. As a result our correlograms don't always appear as clear cut as our examples suggest.

To cope with the problem of trend we have simply subtracted a smooth trend line from each point in the data series. This trend line is calculated from the original series using a repeated sliding average or running mean. The procedure is to calculate, for each year in the series, a new value based on an average of the old value, the two preceding values and the two subsequent ones. This gives a new smoother series. Doing this again and again gradually cuts down the fluctuations and after repeating the process ten times, a curving trend line is produced (Fig 33.4). The values along this trend line are then subtracted from the original data set to give an entirely trend free series.

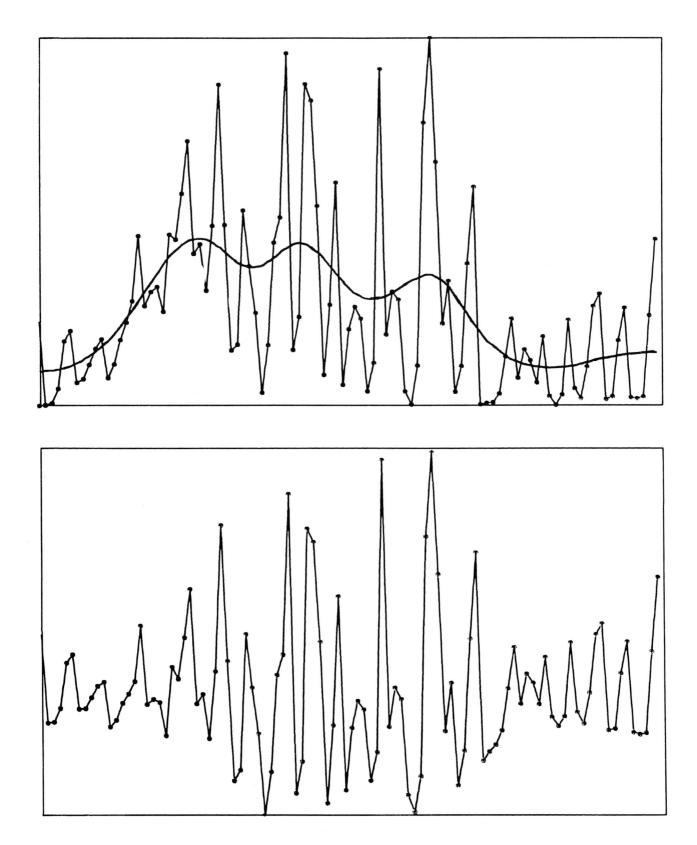

Fig 33.4 Removing trend from bag records. Top; the original 100 years of bag records (red grouse) and the smooth calculated trend line. Below; the detrended series calculated by subtracting the smooth curve from the original series.

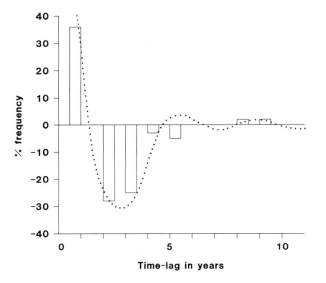

Fig 33.5 The number of significant auto-correlation coefficients plotted by time interval (bars). The dotted line suggests how these would fit to a damped quasi-cycle of about 4.5 years. (From analysis of grouse bag data from 68 moors).

The second problem, that of interpreting the correlogram, is more difficult to deal with. It is simple enough to define a region around the baseline of the correlogram within which we will regard coefficients as not significantly different from zero. Indeed we can calculate two standard errors above and below this zero line to give us a 95% confidence region. Coefficients that fall outside this region are therefore likely to be significant if they also fit into a cyclic pattern on the correlogram. However, with individual sets of records, it may still not be very clear. But if we have several data sets, where we expect them to be acting in a similar fashion, we can combine the occurrences of significant coefficients into a simple bar chart to see if they fit a pattern. Fig 33.5 shows where we have done this for sets of red grouse data. If all these grouse bag-records had been fluctuating at random we would have expected a few significant coefficients at all time intervals simply through chance. We also would expect to see a large number of positive coefficients at time interval one if the series were of type 4B. What we found was a large number of significant negative coefficients at intervals 2 and 3, indicating phase-forgetting quasi-cycles with a period of about 5 years.

The above approach, detrending, calculation of correlograms and a frequency distribution of the coefficients from combined sets of data, is the one we have used for those species where we have long sets of data and a tendency to cycle. To many non-population biologists this all may seem rather mind stretching. To the mathematical ecologists our approach is more likely to seem unsophisticated and crude. What we hope we have done is to get some understanding of the nature of population cycles and time series analysis across to the bulk of our readers. We hope we haven't fallen between two stools.

James Pinnock, head of the Holkham Beaters.

APPENDIX III

THE NATIONAL GAME BAG CENSUS COMPUTER

The first computer system that The Game Conservancy purchased in 1977 was a small Mini—in fact a desk-top version of the successful Wang 2200 series of machines. This used a version of the BASIC programming language integrated with a disk operating system which was "hardwired" into a ROM. This interpreter and operating system took up some 64K of memory, allowing the user only 8K for programs and data storage. Two small diskette drives were mounted on top and this machine was the first in Britain to use 5.25 inch diskettes—8 inch being the previous standard.

The printer was in fact a plotting typewriter based on an IBM Selectric (golf-ball) machine. Additional servo motors allowed the platen to roll backwards and forwards, and the golf-ball to travel side to side so that points could be plotted in small steps using a specially centred dot. This machine, when operating as a printer gave rather slow output but provided you could write the programs it was capable of producing an accurate plot. Indeed, we completed a full time series analysis for the red grouse bags from over 50 north of England moors using with system. Also, using estate grid references data could be plotted onto standard printed base maps of Britain.

Our programs for the National Game Bag Census were written from scratch, but since only 8K of RAM was available and the diskette capacities were only 80K, program design and data storage had to be imaginative to squeeze everything in. The WANG stored its data on disk in precise 256 byte sectors and to use this efficiently records were best stored in single sectors. This was difficult using fixed length fields and allowing space for maximum possible numbers. In fact most estates shot only a small proportion of all possible game species, so instead data were held in 4 alpha-numeric strings. The first (57 bytes) contained a code number, estate name, grid reference, number of gamekeepers, as well as areas of woodland, grouse moor and total area. These fields were at specific fixed intervals along the string. The second, third and fourth strings (64 bytes each) contained details of the bag, rearing, and predators respectively. For these, each species had a code letter followed by the number killed. In this way no space was wasted on empty fields and the record for one place in one year could be squeezed into one sector. Each record was tagged with a code number which was used as a record key, and these record keys were held in an index which could be loaded into memory so individual records could be accessed directly by sector number when required. Because years were stored on different disks, the most used programs were the ones that produced a summary table by species and region for a single year.

The late seventies and early eighties were marked by explosive developments in the computer industry and the invention of the microprocessor caused a radical change in conventional computer thinking. The idea that the wider use of computers would come through bigger and more powerful mainframe machines sharing their processing to an increasing number of terminals was dumped. The price of the new microprocessor based machines meant that one computer per user was a cheaper and more flexible approach. The first micro to really exemplify this approach was the little Apple II. A range of other manufacturers followed this and software companies developed a whole range of applications software. Word-processors, novel data analysis packages called spreadsheets and, particularly interesting to us, database management packages designed for record keeping applications. This in turn set the stage for more powerful micros designed with business and data processing in mind.

These newer machines had 16 bit processors and used Microsoft's MSDOS operating system. The first of this generation of machines to reach Britain was the Sirius I, actually a Victor 9000 marketed and supported by ACT of Birmingham. This machine had a number of sophisticated features which set it ahead of the IBM PC—its early rival. Its 5.25 inch diskettes ran at variable speed, so it could store data at maximum density whether the disk head was operating near the perimeter or the centre of the platter. Using this method 1.25 megabytes were crammed onto a single diskette. The screen resolution was stunning and it had a graphics mode of 800 x 400 pixels. The keyboard was entirely software controlled and different character sets and keyboards could be loaded for separate applications. It was well designed and solidly built with no shortcuts. By comparison the IBM PC was distinctly down-market (even though it was more expensive) with 1960's styling, no graphics, and disks which could only hold 360K.

In 1983 we purchased a Sirius with a 10MB hard disk (later expanded to 30MB) to extend the National Game Bag Census as well as to allow us to use a wider range of applications without having to generate our own programs. To handle the game bag records we chose a product that was rapidly becoming established as the market leader for mainstream database applications—dBase II from Ashton-Tate. The main advantage of this software was that it allowed fairly complex and structured programs to be built, as well having a command language designed for generating database searches and reports. With dBase II such formatting details as sector size are transparent, so files are based on records of a size specified by the user and these are split into labelled fields of any length. Various commands allow selection, sorting and indexing of these records.

We set the game census application up as three main data files. One contained the details of the bag with each record showing numbers of all game shot on one shoot in a particular year. Another file contained similar records of predators, and a third master file contained particulars of the each shoot or estate, the owner's name and address, as well as an indication of which years bag and predator data had been sent in. The key which linked all three files was the code number, and the master file was indexed by code and the other two by code + year and year + code.

Bag details were actually stored as characters to enable us to tack on additional information about the bag in particular instances. For example, the letter "s" tagged onto a number indicated that the total for this species was for shooting days only and therefore not the complete total for the whole year.

Analysis programs were written using the dBase command language and results output to printer or to disk. DBase II was unsuitable for some statistical procedures

and so a few additional programs were written in Microsoft BASIC; for example to calculate confidence limits and to do time series analysis. To represent data graphically we used a package designed for Sirius and Apricot machines called Microchart (Praxis Ltd), and output our data to an A4 flat-bed plotter.

The above was the main system used to run most of the analyses for the results presented in this book, although we have redrawn the figures with a scientific graphics package called Sygraph, using laser printing, and employed another package called Applause II to originate the coloured maps.

In 1991 we transferred the National Game Bag Census database to a new, larger IBM compatible machine (an AST Premium 386) and we are now in the process of re-writing most of the software. We have decided adopt a Windows based environment and use Superbase 4 as the main data handling software. The main advantage of this new system, apart from the sheer calculating speed provided by a modern computer, is that the analyses and report generation can be made more intuitive. This will hopefully encourage a wider range of analyses to be made by biologists whose main forté are field based studies. Furthermore, Windows allows direct links to graphics applications which can be built into the system, for example permitting users to inspect large amount of data graphically, a great advantage with long series of information. A more powerful system also enables us to build up our sample to include a larger number of shoots and estates.

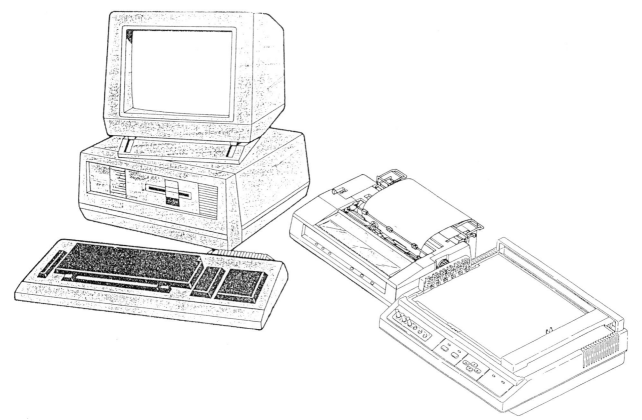

The Sirius (Victor 9000) computer system purchased in 1983 with printer and A4 flat bed plotter.

REFERENCES

AEBISCHER, N.J. (1991) Sustainable yields: gamebirds as a harvestable resource. *Gibier Faune Sauvage*, **6**, 335-351.

AKANDE, M. (1972) The food of feral mink *(Mustela vison)* in Scotland. *Journal of Zoology, London.* **167**, 475-479.

ANDERSEN, J. (1957) Studies in Danish hare populations. I. Population fluctuations. *Danish Review of Game Biology,* **3**, 85-131.

ANDERSEN, P. & YALDEN, D.W. (1981) Increased sheep numbers and the loss of heather moorland in the Peak District. *Biological Conservation*, **30**, 195-213.

ANDREWS, J. & KINSMAN, D. (1990) *Gravel Pit Restoration for Wildlife. A practical manual.* Royal Society for Protection of Birds, Sandy.

ANGELSTAM, P. (1986) Predation on ground nesting birds' nests in relation to predator densities and habitat edge. *Oikos,* **47,** 365-373.

ANON. (1981) *Wildfowl Management on Inland Waterways.* Advisory booklet **3**, The Game Conservancy, Fordingbridge.

ANON (1991) *DJV-Handbuch.* Deutscher Jagdschutz-Verband, Verlag Dieter Hoffman, Mainz.

ARNOLD, H.R. (1978) *Provisional Atlas of the Mammals of the British Isles.* Biological Records Centre, Abbots Ripton.

ARNOLD, H.R. (1984) *Distribution Maps of the Mammals of the British Isles.* Biological Records Centre, Abbots Ripton.

ASH, J.S. (1967) Bag records as indicators of population trends in partridges. *Finnish Game Research,* **30**, 357-360.

BAIN, C. & BAINBRIDGE, I. (1988) A better future for our native pinewoods. *Royal Society for Protection of Birds Conservation Review 1988,* **2**, 50-53.

BAINES D, (1990) The ecology and conservation of black grouse in Scotland and northern England. In: *The Future of Wild Galliformes in the Netherlands.* Eds J.T. Lumeij & Y.R. Hoogeveen. Organisatiecommissie Nederlandse Wilde Hoenders, Amersfoort, Netherlands.

BAINES, D. (1991) Long term changes in the European black grouse population. *The Game Conservancy Review of 1990,* **22,** 157-158.

BAINES, D., GODDARD, J., & HUDSON, P. (1991) Capercaillie in Scotland. *The Game Conservancy Review of 1990,* **22,** 153-156.

BALL, D.F., DALE, J., SHEAIL, J., & HEAL, O.W. (1982) *Vegetation change in upland landscapes.* Report for the Natural Environment Research Council, Institute of Terrestrial Ecology, Cambridge.

BARNES, R.F.W. (1984) *The decline of red grouse bags in Scotland.* Report for the Scottish Grouse Research Committtee, The Game Conservancy, Fordingbridge.

BARNES, R.F.W. (1987) Long-term declines of Red Grouse in Scotland. *Journal of Applied Ecology,* **24,** 735-741.

BARNES, R.F.W. & TAPPER, S.C. (1985) A method for counting hares by spotlight. *Journal of Zoology, London.* **206**, 273-276.

BARNES, R.F.W. & TAPPER, S.C. (1986) Consequences of the myxomatosis epidemic in Britain's *(Oryctolagus cuniculus* L.) population on the numbers of Brown hares *(Lepus europaeus* Pallas). *Mammal Review,* **16**, 111-116.

BEINTEMA, A. & MÜSKENS, G. (1983) Changes in the migration pattern of the Common Snipe. In: *Proceedings of the Second European Woodcock and Snipe Workshop.* Ed. H. Kalchreuter. International Waterfowl Research Bureau, Slimbridge.

BERTELSEN, J. & SIMONSEN, N.H. (1986) *Documentation on Bird Hunting and the Conservation Status of the Species Involved: Situation in 1986.* Report for the Game and Wildlife Administration, Kalø, Denmark.

BETTEY, J.H. (1970) *Rural life in Wessex. 1500 — 1900.* Moonraker Press, Bradford-on-Avon.

BIRKHEAD, T.R. (1986) Magpie. In: *The Atlas of Wintering Birds in Britain and Ireland.* Ed. P. Lack. British Trust for Ornithology, Tring.

BIRKHEAD, T.R. (1991) *The Magpies: The Ecology and Behaviour of Black-billed and Yellow-billed Magpies.* T & A.D. Poyser, London.

BLANCH, H.J. (1909) *A Century of Guns: a sketch of the leading types of sporting and military small arms.* J. Blanch & Son, London.

BLANK, T.H. & ASH, J.S. (1954) A population of partridges *(Perdix p. perdix* and *Alectoris r. rufa)* on a Hampshire estate. *Proceedings of the 11th International Ornithological Congress,* Basel. 424-427.

BLANK, T.H. & ASH, J.S. (1957) Factors controlling the brood size in the partridge *(Perdix perdix)* on an estate in south England. *Proceedings of the 3rd Congress of the International Union of Game Biologists, Danish Review of Game Biology,* **3**, 39-40.

BLANK, T.H., SOUTHWOOD, T.R.E. & CROSS, D.J. (1967) The ecology of the partridge. I. Outline of population processes with particular reference to chick mortality and nest density. *Journal of Animal Ecology,* **36**, 549-556.

BOAG, B. & TAPPER, S. (*in press*) The history of some British game-birds and mammals in relation to agricultural change. *Agricultural Zoology Reviews.*

BRENCHLEY, A. (1986) Rook. In: *The Atlas of Wintering Birds in Britain and Ireland* Ed. P. Lack. British Trust for Ornithology, Tring.

BRITISH GEOLOGICAL SURVEY (1989) *United Kingdom Minerals Yearbook, 1988*. Keyworth, Nottingham.

BROEKHUIZEN, S. (1981) Studies on the population ecology of hares in the Netherlands. *Report of The Research Institute for Nature Management*. Arnhem, Netherlands.

BROWN, L. (1976) *British Birds of Prey*. New Naturalist series, Collins, London

BRYAN, A. (1967) The first people. In: *Alberta: a natural history*. Ed. W.G. Hardy, Mismat, Edmonton, Canada.

BUNYAN, P.J., STANLEY, P.I., BLUNDEN, C.A., WARDALL, G.L. & TARRANT, K.A. (1975) A review of wildlife incidents investigated during the period 1971-1973. *MAFF Pest Infestation Control Laboratory Report 1971-1973*. HMSO.

BURRARD, G. (1932) *The Modern Shotgun: Volume III The Gun and Cartridge*. Herbert Jenkins, London.

CARTER, S. (1991) Waterways bird survey in 1989. In: *Britain's Birds in 1989-90: the conservation and monitoring review*. Eds D. Stroud & D. Glue. British Trust for Ornithology & Nature Conservancy Council, Thetford.

CHANIN, P.R.F. & LINN, I. (1980) The diet of feral mink *(Mustela vison)* in southwest Britain. *Journal of Zoology, London*, **192**, 205-223.

CHARLES, J. (1972) *Territorial behaviour and limitation of population size in the crow* Corvus corone *and* Corvus cornix. Unpublished Ph.D Thesis, University of Aberdeen

CLARKE, S.P. (1970) Field experience of feral mink in Yorkshire and Lancashire. *Mammal Review*, **1**, 41-47.

CLARKSON, K. & BIRKHEAD, T. (1987) Magpies in Sheffield — a recipe for success. *British Trust for Ornithology News*, **151**, 8-9.

CLAUSAGER, I. (1983) Wing collection of woodcock in Denmark. In: *Proceedings of the Second European Woodcock and Snipe Workshop,* Ed. H. Kalchreuter. International Wildfowl Research Bureau, Slimbridge.

COATS, A. (1963) Pigeon shooting. *Field Sports Handbooks*. Ed. C. Willock. Vista Books, London.

COBHAM RESOURCE CONSULTANTS (1992) *Countryside Sports: Their Economic and Conservation Significance*. Standing Conference on Countryside Sports, College of Estate Management, Reading.

COOK, A. (1975) Changes in the carrion/hooded crow hybrid zone and the possible importance of climate. *Bird Study*, **22**, 165-168.

CORBET, G.B. (1986) The relationships and origins of the European lagomorphs. *Mammal Review*, **16**, 105-110

CRAMP, S. & SIMMONS, K.E.L. (1982) *The Birds of the Western Palearctic Vol III*. Oxford University Press, Oxford.

CRUDGINGTON, I.M. & BAKER, D.J. (1979) *The British Shotgun: Volume One 1850-1870*. Barrie & Jenkins, London.

CUTHBERT, J.H. (1973) The origin and distribution of feral mink in Scotland. *Mammal Review*, **3**, 97-103.

DAY, M.G. (1968) Food habits of British stoats *(Mustela erminea)* and weasels *(Mustela nivalis)*. *Journal of Zoology, London*, **155**, 485-497.

DEANESLY, R. (1943) Delayed implantation in the stoat *(Mustela mustela)*. *Nature,* **151**, 365-366.

DEGN, H.J. (1978) The Danish population of black grouse. *Woodland Grouse Symposium*. Ed. T.W.I. Lovel. The World Pheasant Association, Suffolk.

DIAMOND, J.M. (1991) Twilight of Hawaiian birds. *Nature,* **535**, 505-506.

DUNLAP, T.R. (1988) *Saving America's Wildlife*. Princeton University Press.

DUNN, E. (1977) Predation by weasels *(Mustela nivalis)* on breeding tits *(Parus spp.)* in relation to density of tits and rodents. *Journal of Animal Ecology*, **46**, 633-651.

EASTERBEE, N., HEPBURN, L.V., & JEFFERIES, D.J. (1991) *Survey of the Status and Distribution of the Wildcat in Scotland, 1983-1987*. Report of the Nature Conservancy Council for Scotland, Edinburgh.

EDEN, R. (1979) *Going to the Moors*. John Murray, London.

ELTON, C. (1942) *Voles, Mice and Lemmings: problems in population dymanics*. Oxford University Press, Oxford.

ELTON, C. & NICHOLSON, M. (1942) The ten-year cycle in numbers of the lynx in Canada. *Journal of Animal Ecology*, **11**, 215-244.

ERLINGE, S. (1974) Distribution, territoriality and numbers of the weasel *Mustela nivalis* in relation to prey abundance. *Oikos*, **25**, 308-314.

ERLINGE, S. (1983) Demography and dynamics of a stoat *Mustela erminea* population in a diverse community of vertebrates. *Journal of Animal Ecology*, **52**, 705-726.

ERLINGE, S. & SANDELL, M. (1986) Seasonal changes in the social organization of male stoats *Mustela erminea*: an effect of shifts between two decisive resources. *Oikos,* **47**, 57-62.

ESTES, J.A., RATHBUN, G., & VAN BLARICOM, G. *(in press)* Paradigms for managing Carnivores: the case of the sea otter. *Symposium of the Zoological Society of London*.

FARGHER, S.E. (1977) The distribution of the brown hare *(Lepus capensis)* and the mountain hare in the Isle of Man. *Journal of Zoology, London*, **182**, 164-167.

FEARE, C.J. (1974) Ecological studies of the rook *(Corvus frugilegus* L.) in north-east Scotland. Damage and control. *Journal of Applied Ecology*, **11**, 897-914.

FEARE, C.J., DUNNET, G.M. & PATTERSON, I.J. (1974) Ecological studies of the rook *(Corvus frugilegus* L.) in north-east Scotland: food intake and feeding behaviour. *Journal of Applied Ecology*, **11**, 867-896.

FENNER, F. & CHAPPLE, P.J. (1965) Evolutionary changes in myxoma virus in Britain. *Journal of Hygiene*, **63**, 175-185.

FIECHTER, A. & BEMMERGUI, M. (1986) Le prélevement cynégétique de lièvres en France. Saison 1983-1984. *Bulletin Mensuel, Office National de la Chasse*, **108**, 33-38.

FINERTY, J.P. (1980) *The population ecology of cycles in small mammals.* Yale University Press, New Haven & London.

FLUX, J.E.C. (1967) Reproduction and body weights of the hare *Lepus europaeus* in New Zealand. *New Zealand Journal of Science,* **10**, 357-401.

FLUX, J.E.C. (1970) Life history of the mountain hare *(Lepus timidus scoticus)* in north-east Scotland. *Journal of Zoology, London,* **161**, 75-123.

FOG, M. (1963) Distribution and food of the Danish rooks. *Danish Review of Game Biology,* **4**, 63-110.

FORD, J., CHITTY, H., & MIDDLETON, A.D. (1938) The food of partridge chicks *(Perdix perdix)* in Great Britain. *Journal of Animal Ecology,* **7**, 251-265.

FRYER, F.E.R. (1903) The partridge: its management, etc., on a driving estate. In: *Shooting. The ''Country Life'' Library of Sport.* Ed. H.G. Hutchinson. Country Life, London.

FRYLESTAM, B. (1976) The European hare in Sweden. In: *The Ecology and Management of European Hare Populations.* Eds Z. Pielowski & Z. Pucek. Polish Hunting Association, Warsaw.

FRYLESTAM, B. (1979) Structure, size, and dynamics of three European hare populations in southern Sweden. *Acta Theriologica,* **24**, 33, 449-464.

FRYLESTAM, B. (1980) Reproduction in the European hare in southern Sweden. *Holarctic Ecology,* **3**, 74-80.

GILES, N. (1989) Experiments on substrate choice and feeding efficiency of downy Tufted ducklings *Aythya fuligula. Wildfowl,* **40**, 74-79.

GILES, N. (1990) Effects of increasing larval chironomid densities on the underwater feeding success of downy Tufted ducks *Aythya fuligula. Wildfowl,* **41**, 90-105.

GILES, N., STREET, M., & WRIGHT, R.M. (1990) Diet composition and prey preference for tench *Tinca tinca* (L), commom bream *Abramis brama* (L), perch *Perca fluviatilis* (L) and roach *Rutilis rutilis* (L) in two contrasting gravel pit lakes : potential trophic overlap with wildfowl. *Journal of Fish Biology,* **37**, 945-957.

GILES, R.H. (1971) *Wildlife Management Techniques.* The Wildlife Society, Washington.

GOOCH, S., BAILLIE, S.R. & BIRKHEAD, T.R. (1991) Magpie *Pica pica* and songbird populations. Retrospective investigation of trends in population density and breeding success. *Journal of Applied Ecology,* **28**, 1068-1086.

GRAY, N. (1986) *Woodland management for pheasants and wildlife.* David & Charles, Newton Abbot.

GREEN, R.E. (1984a) The feeding ecology and survival of partridge chicks *(Alectoris rufa* and *Perdix perdix)* on arable farmland in East Anglia. *Journal of Applied Ecology,* **21**, 817-830.

GREEN, R.E. (1984b) Double nesting of the Red-legged partridge *Alectoris rufa. Ibis,* **126**, 332-346.

GREEN, R.E. (1985) Estimating the abundance of breeding snipe. *Bird Study,* **32**, 141-149.

GREEN, R.E., HAWELL, J., & JOHNSON, T.H. (1987) Identification of predators of wader eggs from egg remains. *Bird Study,* **34**, 87-91.

GROVE, S.J., HOPE JONES, P., MALKINSON, A.R., THOMAS, D.H. & WILLIAMS, I. (1988) Black grouse in Wales. *British Birds,* **81**, 2-9.

GURNELL, J. (1987) *The Natural History of Squirrels.* Christopher Helm, Beckenham.

HARRADINE, J.(1985) Duck shooting in the United Kingdom. *Wildfowl,* **36**, 81-94.

HARRADINE, J.(1986) Jack Snipe. In: *The Atlas of Wintering Birds in Britain and Ireland* Ed. P. Lack. British Trust for Ornithology, Tring.

HARRIS, S. & RAYNER, J.M.V. (1986) Urban fox *(Vulpes vulpes)* population estimates and habitat requirements in several cities. *Journal of Animal Ecology,* **55**, 575-591.

HARVEY, N. (1987) *Fields, Hedges and Ditches.* Shire Publications, Aylesbury.

HEWSON, R. (1964) Reproduction in the brown hare and the mountain hare in north-east Scotland. *The Scottish Naturalist,* **71**, 81-89.

HEWSON, R. (1984) Changes in the numbers of foxes *(Vulpes vulpes)* in Scotland. *Journal of Zoology, London,* **204**, 561-569.

HEWSON, R. (1986) Distribution and density of fox breeding dens and the effects of management. *Journal of Applied Ecology,* **23**, 531-538.

HEWSON, R. (1991) The Mountain hare *(Lepus timidus).* In: *The Handbook of British Mammals 3rd Edition.* Eds G.B. Corbet & S. Harris. Blackwell Scientific Publications, Oxford.

HEWSON, R. & HEALING, T.D. (1971) The stoat *Mustela erminea* and its prey. *Journal of Zoology,* London, **164**, 239-270.

HEWSON, R. & KOLB, H.H. (1973) Changes in the numbers and distribution of foxes *(Vulpes vulpes)* killed in Scotland from 1948-1970. *Journal of Zoology,* London, **171**, 345-365.

HEWSON, R. & TAYLOR, M. (1975) Embryo counts and length of the breeding season in the European hares in Scotland from 1960-1972. *Acta Theriologica,* **20**, 247-254.

HILL, D.A. (1984) Population regulation in the Mallard *(Anas platyrhynchos). Journal of Animal Ecology,* **53**, 191-202.

HILL, D.A. (1985) The feeding ecology and survival of pheasant chicks on arable farmland. *Journal of Applied Ecology,* **22**, 645-654.

HILL, D. & ROBERTSON, P. (1988) *The Pheasant: Ecology, management and conservation.* Blackwell Scientific Publications, Oxford.

HILL, D., WRIGHT, R. & STREET, M. (1987) Survival of Mallard ducklings *Anas platyrhynchos* and competition with fish for invertebrates on a flooded gravel quarry in England. *Ibis,* **129**, 159-167.

HIRONS, G. (1983) A five year study of the breeding behaviour and biology of the woodcock in England — a first report. In: *Proceedings of the 2nd European Woodcock and Snipe Workshop.* Ed. H. Kalchreuter. International Waterfowl Research Bureau, Slimbridge.

HIRONS, G. & BICKFORD-SMITH, P. (1983) The diet and behaviour of Eurasian woodcock wintering in Cornwall. In: *Proceedings of the 2nd European Woodcock and Snipe workshop.* Ed. H. Kalchreuter. International Waterfowl Research Bureau, Slimbridge.

HJORTH, I. (1982) Attributes of Capercaillie display grounds and the influence of forestry. In: *Proceedings of the 2nd International Symposium on Grouse.* Ed. T.W.I. Lovel. The World Pheasant Association, Suffolk.

HOLYOAK, D. (1968) A comparative study of the food of some British Corvidae. *Bird Study,* **15**, 147-153.

HOLYOAK, D. (1974) Territorial and feeding behaviour of the magpie. *Bird Study,* **21**, 117-128.

HORN, P. (1984) *The Changing Countryside in Victorian and Edwardian England and Wales.* The Athlone Press, London.

HOUSTON, D.C. (1986) Carrion Crow/Hooded Crow. In: *The Atlas of Wintering Birds in Britain and Ireland.* Ed. P. Lack. British Trust for Ornithology, Tring.

HUDSON, P. (1986a) *Red Grouse, the Biology and Management of a Wild Gamebird.* The Game Conservancy, Fordingbridge.

HUDSON, P.J. (1986b) The effect of a parasite nematode on the breeding production of red grouse. *Journal of Animal Ecology,* **55**, 85-92.

HUDSON, P.J. (1990) Territorial status and survival in a low density grouse population. In: *Red Grouse Population Processes.* Eds. A.N. Lance & J.H. Lawton. British Ecological Society & Royal Society of Protection of Birds, Oxford.

HUDSON, P. (1992) *Grouse in Space and Time: the population biology of a managed gamebird.* The Game Conservancy, Fordingbridge.

HUDSON P.J., & DOBSON, A.P. (1990) Red grouse population cycles and population dynamics of the caecal nematode *Trichostrongylus tenuis.* In: *Red Grouse Populations Processes.* Eds A.N. Lance & J.H. Lawton. British Ecological Society & Royal Society for Protection of Birds, Oxford.

INGLIS, I.R., ISAACSON, A.J., THEARLE, R.J.P. & WESTWOOD, N.J. (1990) The effects of changing agricultural practice upon woodpigeon numbers. *Ibis,* **132**, 262-272.

INGLIS, I.R., THREARLE, R.J.P, & ISAACSON, A.J. (1989) Woodpigeon *(Columba palumbus)* damage to oilseed rape. *Crop Protection,* **8**, 299-309.

JEFFERIES, D.J., MORRIS, P.A., & MULLENEUX, J.E. (1989) An equiry into the changing status of the water vole *Arvicola terrestris* in Britian. *Mammal Review,* **19**, 111-131.

JEFFERIES, D.J. & PENDLEBURY, J.B. (1968) Population fluctuations of stoats, weasels and hedgehogs in recent years. *Journal of Zoology, London,* **156**, 513-517.

JEFFERIES, D.J. & PRESST, I. (1966) Post-mortems of peregrines and lanners with particular reference to organochlorine residues. *British Birds,* **59**, 49-64.

JENKINS, D. (1962) The present status of the wild cat *(Felis sylvestris)* in Scotland. *The Scottish Naturalist,* **70**, 126-138.

JENKINS, D., WATSON, A., & MILLAR, G.R. (1964) Predation and red grouse populations. *Journal of Applied Ecology,* **1**, 183-195.

JENSEN, A. & JENSEN, B. (1972) The polecat *(Putorius putorius)* in Denmark. *Dansk Vildtundersøgelser,* **18**, 1-32.

JOHN, A. (1986) Jay. In: *The Atlas of wintering birds in Britain and Ireland* Ed. P. Lack. British Trust for Ornithology, Tring.

JOHN, A.W.G. & ROSKELL, J. (1985) Jay movements in autumn 1983. British Birds, **78**, 611-637.

JOHNSGARD, P. A. (1986) *The pheasants of the world.* Oxford University Press, Oxford.

KALCHREUTER, H. (1979) *Die Waldschnepfe.* Verlag Dieter Hoffman, Mainz.

KASTDALEN, L. & WEGGE, P. (1984) Animal food in Capercaillie and Black Grouse chicks in South East Norway — a preliminary report. In: *Proceedings of the 3rd International Grouse Symposium.* Eds T. Lovel, & P. Hudson, World Pheasant Association, Suffolk.

KEITH, L.B. (1963) *Wildlife's ten-year cycle.* The University of Wisconsin Press, Madison.

KEITH, L.B., TODD, A.W., BRAND, C.J., ADAMCIK, R.S. & RUSCH, D.H. (1977) An analysis of predation during a cyclic fluctuation of Snowshoe hares. In: *Proceedings of the 13th Congress of the International Union of Game Biologists.* Ed. T.J. Peterle. The Wildlife Society, Washington.

KENWARD, R.E. & PARISH, T. (1986) Bark-stripping by grey squirrels *(Sciurus carolinensis). Journal of Zoology, London,* **210**, 473-481.

KENWARD, R.E., PARISH, T., HOLM, J. & HARRIS, E.H.M. (1988) Grey squirrel bark-stripping I. The roles of tree quality, squirrel learning and food abundance. *Quarterly Journal of Forestry,* **82**, 9-20.

KENWARD, R.E., PARISH, T. & ROBERTSON, P.A. (1992) Are tree species too good for grey squirrels? In: *Ecology of mixed-species stands of trees.* Eds M.G.R. Cannell, D.C. Malcolm & P.A. Robertson. Blackwell, Scientific Publications, Oxford.

KING, C.M. (1975a) The sex-ratio of trapped weasels *(Mustela nivalis). Mammal Review,* **5**, 1-8.

KING, C.M. (1975b) Home-range of the weasel *(Mustela nivalis)* in an English woodland. *Journal of Animal Ecology,* **44**, 639-668.

KING, C.M. (1980a) The weasel *Mustela nivalis* and its prey in an English woodland. *Journal of Animal Ecology,* **49**, 127-159.

KING, C.M. (1980b) Population biology of the weasel *Mustela nivalis* on British game estates. *Holarctic Ecology,* **3**, 160-168.

KING, C. (1984) *Immigrant killers: introduced predators and the conservation of birds in New Zealand.* Oxford University Press, Auckland.

KING, C.M. & MOORS, P.J. (1979) On co-existence, foraging strategy and biogeography of weasels and stoats *(Mustela nivalis* and *M.erminea)* in Britain. *Oecologia,* **39**, 129-150.

KING, P. (1985) *The Shooting Field: one hundred and fifty years with Holland & Holland.* Quiller Press, London.

KOLB, H.H. & HEWSON, R. (1980) A study of fox populations in Scotland from 1971 to 1976. *Journal of Applied Ecology,* **17**, 7-19.

LACK, P. (1986) *The Atlas of Wintering Birds in Britain and Ireland.* T. & A.D. Poyser, Calton.

LANCUM F.H. (1951) *Wild Mammals and the Land.* MAFF Bulletin No. 150, HMSO.

LANGLEY, P.J.W. & YALDEN, D.W. (1977) The decline of the rarer carnivores in Great Britain during the nineteenth century. *Mammal Review,* **7**, 95-116.

LEOPOLD, A. (1933) *Game Management.* Scribner's, New York.

LEOPOLD, A. (1949) *A Sand County Almanac, and Sketches Here and There.* Oxford University Press, New York.

LEVER, C. (1977) *The naturalized animals of the British Isles.* Hutchinson, London.

LEVER, R.J.A.W. (1959) The diet of the fox since myxomatosis. *Journal of Animal Ecology,* **28**, 359-375.

LINDSTROM, E., ANDREN, H., ANGELSTAM, P. & WIDEN P. (1986) Influence of predators on hare populations in Sweden. *Mammal Review,* **16**, 151-156.

LLOYD, H.G. (1980) *The Red Fox.* Batsford, London.

LOCKE, G.M.L. (1987) *Census of Woodlands and Trees 1979-82.* Forestry Commission Bulletin, **63**, HMSO, London.

LOCKLEY, R.M. (1964) *The Private Life of the Rabbit.* Andre Deutsch, London.

LONGRIGG, R. (1977) *The English Squire and his Sport.* Michael Joseph, London.

LOVAT, LORD (1911) *The Grouse in Health and in Disease. Vol. I.* The final report of the committee of inquiry on grouse disease. Smith, Elder & Co., London.

MACKENZIE, J.M.D. (1952) Fluctuations in the numbers of British tetraonids. *Journal of Animal Ecology,* **21**, 128-153

MARCHANT, J.H., HUDSON R., CARTER S.P. & WHITTINGTON P. (1990) *Population Trends in British Breeding Birds.* British Trust for Ornithology, Tring.

MARCSTROM, V. (1978) A review of the Tetraonid situation in Sweden. In: *Woodland Grouse Symposium.* Ed. T.W.I. Lovel. The World Pheasant Association, Suffolk.

MARTIN, P.S. (1967) Prehistoric overkill. In: *Pleistocene extinctions: the search for a cause.* Eds. P.S. Martin & H.E. Wright. Yale University Press, Yale.

MASON, C.F. & MACDONALD, S.M. (1976) Aspects of the breeding biology of the snipe. *Bird Study,* **23**, 33-38.

MATHESON, C. (1962) *Brown rats.* Sunday Times Publications, London.

MAXWELL, A. (1911) *Partridges and partridge manors.* Adam & Charles Black, London.

McKELVIE, C.L. (1986) *The book of the Woodcock.* Debrett's Peerage, London.

MEAD-BRIGGS, A.R. & RUDGE, A.J.B. (1960) Breeding of the rabbit flea, *Spipsyllus cuniculi* (Dale): requirement of a "factor" from a pregnant rabbit for ovarian maturation. *Nature,* **187**, 1136-1137.

MEAD-BRIGGS, A.R. & VAUGHAN, J.A. (1975) The differential transmissibility of myxoma virus strains of differing virulence grades by the rabbit flea *Spilopsyllus cuniculi* (Dale). *Journal of Hygiene, Cambridge,* **75**, 237-247.

MIDDLETON, A.D. (1931) *The grey squirrel.* Sidgwick & Jackson, London.

MIDDLETON, A.D. (1934) Periodic fluctuations in British game populations. *Journal of Animal Ecology,* **3**, 231-249.

MIDDLETON, A.D. (1936) Factors controlling the population of the partridge *(Perdix perdix)* in Great Britain. *Proceedings of the Zoological Society of London,* **106**, 795-815.

MOORE, N.W. (1956) Rabbits buzzards and hares. Two studies on the indirect effects of myxomatosis. *La Terre et la Vie,* **103**, 220-225.

MOORS, P.J. (1975) The food of weasels *(Mustela nivalis)* on farmland in north-east Scotland. *Journal of Zoology,* **177**, 455-461.

MORRIS, P.A. (1973) Winter nests of the hedgehog *(Erinaceus europaeus* L.). *Oecologia,* **11**, 299-313.

MORRIS, P.A. (1977) Hedgehog. *Erinaceus europaeus.* In: *The Handbook of British Mammals — 2nd Edition.* Eds. G.B. Corbet & H.N. Southern. Blackwells Scientific Publications, Oxford.

MORRISON, C. (1989) *Game 2000: A manifesto for the future of Game in Britain.* A pamphlet by The Game Conservancy, Fordingbridge.

MOSS, R. & WATSON, A. (1985) Adaptive value of spacing behaviour in population cycles of red grouse and other animals. In: *Behavioural Ecology — Ecological Consequences of Adaptive Behaviour.* Eds R.M. Sibly & R.H. Smith. Blackwells, Oxford.

MOSS R. & WATSON, A. (1990) Population regulation in red grouse - a theoretical outline. In: *Red Grouse Population Processes.* Eds A.N. Lance & J.H. Lawton. British Ecological Society & Royal Society of Protection of Birds, Oxford.

MOSS, R., WEIR, D. & JONES, A. (1979) Capercaillie management in Scotland. In: *Woodland Grouse Symposium.* Ed. T.W.I Lovel. Word Pheasant Association, Suffolk.

MURSELL, N. (1981) *Come Dawn, Come Dusk: 50 years a gamekeeper.* Allen & Unwin, London.

MURTON, R.K. (1965) *The Woodpigeon.* Collins, London.

MURTON, R.K., ISAACSON, A.J. & WESTWOOD, N.J. (1966) The relationship between woodpigeons and their clover food supply and the mechanism of population control. *Journal of Applied Ecology,* **3**, 55-96.

NAPIER, A., (1903) Pheasants at Holkham. In: *Shooting. The "Country Life" Library of Sport.* Ed. H.G. Hutchinson. Country Life, London.

NEWTON, I. (1979) *Population Ecology of Raptors.* T. & A.D. Poyser, Berkhampstead.

NIEWOLD, F.J.J. (1990) The decline of black grouse in the Netherlands. In: *The Future of Wild Galliformes in the Netherlands* Eds J.T. Lumeij & Y.R. Hoogeveen. Organisatiecommissie Nederlandse Wilde Hoenders, Amersfoort, Netherlands.

NISBET, R.M. & GURNEY, W.S.C. (1982) *Modelling fluctuating populations.* John Wiley & Sons, Chichester.

O'CONNER, R.J. & SHRUBB, M. (1986) *Farming and birds.* Cambridge University Press, Cambridge.

OGILVIE, M.A. (1986a) Teal *(Anas crecca)* In: *The Atlas of Wintering Birds in Britain and Ireland.* Ed. P. Lack. T. & A.D. Poyser, Calton.

OGILVIE, M.A. (1986b) Tufted duck *(Aythya fuligula)* In: *The Atlas of Wintering Birds in Britain and Ireland.* Ed. P. Lack. T. & A.D. Poyser, Calton.

OSBORNE, P. (1982) Some effects of Dutch Elm disease on nesting farmland birds. *Bird Study,* **29**, 2-16.

OWEN, M., ATKINSON-WILLES, G.L. & SALMON, D.G. (1986) *Wildfowl in Great Britain.* Cambridge University Press, Cambridge.

PAGE, R.J.C. (1981) Dispersal and population density of the fox *(Vulpes vulpes)* in an area of London. *Journal of Zoology,* **194**, 485-491.

PAYNE-GALLWEY, R. (1902) *Letters to Young Shooters. Second Series, on the Production, Preservation, and Killing of Game, with Directions in Shooting Woodpigeons and Breaking in Retrievers.* Longmans, Green and Co., London.

PEGEL, M. (1986) *Der Feldhase* (Lepus europaeus *Pallas) im Beziehungsgefüge seiner Um- und Mitweltfaktoren.* Schriften des Arbeitskreises Wildbiologie und Jagdwissenschaft an der Justus-Liebig-Universität, Giessen. Heft 16.

PICOZZI, N. (1986) *Black grouse research in N.E. Scotland.* Institute of Terrestrial Ecology Report, Banchory.

PIDDINGTON, H. R. (1981) *Land management for shooting and fishing. A study of practice on farms and estates in Great Britain 1971-76.* Occasional paper No. 13, Department of Land Economy, University of Cambridge.

POLLARD, E., HOOPER, M.D. & MOORE, N.W. (1974) *Hedges.* Collins, London.

POLLARD, H.B.C. (1923) *Shot-guns: their history and development.* Pittman & Sons, London.

POTTS, G.R. (1980) The effects of modern agriculture, nest predation and game management on the population ecology of partridges, *Perdix perdix* and *Alectoris rufa. Advances in Ecological Research,* **11**, 1-82.

POTTS, G.R. (1986) *The Partridge. Pesticides, predation and conservation.* Collins, London.

POTTS, G.R., TAPPER, S.C. & HUDSON, P.J. (1984) Population fluctuations in red grouse: analysis of bag records and a simulation model. *Journal of Animal Ecology,* **53**, 21-36.

POTTS, G.R. & VICKERMAN, G.P. (1974) Studies on the cereal ecosystem. *Advances in Ecological Research,* **8**, 107-197.

PRESTT, I. & MILLS, D.H. (1966) A census of the great crested grebe in Britain: 1965. *Bird Study,* **13**, 163-203.

RANDS, M.R.W. (1985) Pesticide use on cereals and the survival of grey partridge chicks: a field experiment. *Journal of Applied Ecology,* **22**, 49-54.

RANDS, M.R.W. (1986) Effect of hedgerow characteristics on partridge breeding densities. *Journal of Applied Ecology,* **23**, 479-487.

REEVE, N.J. & MORRIS, P.A. (1985) Construction and use of summer nests by the hedgehog *(Erinaceus europaeus). Mammalia,* **49**, 187-194.

REIDMAN, M.L. & ESTES, J.A. (1990) *The Sea Otter (*Enhydra lutris*): behaviour, ecology, and natural history.* Biological Report 19 (14), U.S. Dept of Interior, Fish and Wildlife Service, Washington.

REIGER, J.F. (1986) *American Sportsmen and the Origins of Conservation.* University of Oklahoma Press, Norman, Oklahoma.

REYNOLDS, J.C. (1985) Details of the geographic replacement of the red squirrel *(Sciurus vulgaris)* by the grey squirrel *(Sciurus carolinensis)* in eastern England. *Journal of Animal Ecology,* **54**, 149-162.

REYNOLDS, J.C., ANGELSTAM, P., & REDPATH, S. (1988) Predators, their ecology and impact on gamebird populations. In: *Ecology and Management of Gamebirds.* Eds P.J. Hudson & M.R.W. Rands. Blackwell Scientific Publications, Oxford.

ROBERTSON, P. (1991) Wise use and conservation. *Gibier Faune Sauvage,* **8**, 379-388.

ROBERTSON, P.A. & DOWELL, S.D. (1990) The effects of hand-rearing on wild gamebird populations. In: *The Future of Wild Galliformes in the Netherlands.* Eds. J.T. Lumeij & Y.R. Hoogeveen. Organisatiecommissie Nederlandse Wilde Hoenders, Amersfoort, Netherlands.

ROBERTSON P.A. & ROSENBERG, A.A. (1988) Harvesting gamebirds. In: *Ecology and Management of Gamebirds.* Eds P.J. Hudson & M.R.W. Rands. Blackwell Scientific Publications, Oxford.

ROBERTSON, P.A., WOODBURN, M.I.A., & HILL, D.A. (1988) The effects of woodland management for pheasants on the abundance of butterflies in Dorset, England. *Biological Conservation,* **45**, 159-167.

ROPPEL, A.Y. & DAVEY, S.P. (1965) Evolution of fur seal management of the Pribilof Islands. *Journal of Wildlife Management,* **29**, 448-463.

ROSS, J. (1972) Myxomatosis and the rabbit. *British Veterinary Journal,* **128**, 172-176.

ROSS, J. & SANDERS, M.F. (1984) The development of genetic resistance to myxomatosis in wild rabbits in Britain. *Journal of Hygiene, Cambridge,* **92**, 255-261.

ROTHSCHILD, M. & MARSH, H. (1956) Increase of hares *(Lepus europaeus* Pallas) at Aston wold, with a note on the reduction in numbers of brown rat *(Rattus norvegicus* Berkenhout). *Proceedings of the Zoological Society of London,* **127**, 441-445.

RUFFER, J.G. (1989) *The Big Shots: Edwardian Shooting Parties.* Quiller Press, London.

SAGE, B.L. & VERNON, J.D.R. (1978) The 1975 national census of rookeries. *Bird Study,* **25**, 64-86

SAGE, B. & WHITTINGTON, P.A. (1985) The 1980 sample survey of rookeries. *Bird Study,* **32**, 77-81.

SALZMANN-WANDELER, I. (1976) Feldhasen-Abshusszahlen in der Schweiz. In: *Ecology and Management of Brown Hare Populations.* Eds Z. Pucek & Z. Pielowski. Polish Hunting Association, Warsaw.

SCOTT, G. (1937) *Grouse Land and the Fringe of the Moor.* H.F. & G. Witherby, London.

SHARROCK, J.T.R. (1976) *The Atlas of Breeding Birds in Britain and Ireland.* British Trust for Ornithology, Tring.

SHEAIL, J. (1971) Changes in the supply of wild rabbits, 1790-1910. *The Agricultural History Review,* **19,** 175-177.

SHORTEN, M. (1954) *Squirrels.* The New Naturalist Series, Collins, London.

SHORTEN, M. (1974) *The European woodcock* (Scalopax rusticola). *Report on a search of the literature since 1940.* The Game Conservancy, Fordingbridge.

SIMPSON, J. (1903) *The New Forestry: or the continental system adapted to British woodlands and game preservation.* Pawson & Brailsford, Sheffield.

SMITH, K.W. (1983) The status and distribution of waders breeding on wet lowland grasslands in England and Wales. *Bird Study,* **30,** 177-192.

SMITH, T. & POLACHECK, T. (1981) Re-examination of the life table for Northern fur seals with implications about population regulatory mechanisms. In: *Dynamics of Large Mammal Populations.* Eds C.W. Fowler & T.D. Smith. J. Wiley & Sons, New York.

SOTHERTON, N.W. (1991) Conservation headlands: a practical combination of intensive cereal farming and conservation. In: *Ecology of Temperate Cereal Fields.* Eds L.G. Firbank, N. Carter, J.F. Darbyshire & G.R. Potts. British Ecological Society Symposium, Blackwell Scientific Publications, Oxford.

SOTHERTON, N.W., BOATMAN, N.D. & RANDS, M.R.W. (1989) The "Conservation Headland" experiment in cereal ecosystems. *The Entomologist,* **108,** 135-143.

SOUTHWOOD, T.R.E. (1967) The ecology of the partridge. II. The role of pre-hatching influences. *Journal of Animal Ecology,* **36,** 557-562.

SOUTHWOOD, T.R.E. & CROSS, D.J. (1969) The ecology of the partridge. III. Breeding success and the abundance of insects in natural habitats. *Journal of Animal Ecology,* **38,** 497-509.

STANFORD, J.K. (1963) *Partridge Shooting.* The Shooting Times Library, No. 4. Percival Marshall, London.

STRACHAN, R., BIRKS, J.D.S., CHANIN, P.R.F., & JEFFERIES, D.J. (1990) *Otter Survey of England.* Report of the Nature Conservancy Council, Peterborough.

STRAKER, H. & LEALAND, B. (1990) *Gamebird Rearing.* Advisory booklet **8,** The Game Conservancy, Fordingbridge.

STRANDGAARD, H. & ASFERG, T. (1980) The Danish bag record. II. Fluctuations and trends in the Game Bag Record in the years 1941-1976 and the geographical distribution of the bag in 1976. *Danish Review of Game Biology,* **11,** 1-112.

STREET, M. (1977) The role of insects in the diet of Mallard ducklings — an experimental approach. *Wildfowl,* **29,** 93-100.

STREET, M. (1983) *The restoration of gravel pits for wildfowl.* ARC Wildfowl Centre, Milton Keynes.

STREET, M. & TITMUS, G. (1982) A field experiment on the value of allochthonous straw as food and substratum for lake macro-invertebrates. *Freshwater Biology,* **12,** 403-410.

STUART-WHORTLEY, A.J. (1894) Shooting. In: *Fur Feather and Fin Series. The Grouse.* Ed. A.E.T Watson. Longman, Green, and Co., London.

SUMPTION, K.J. & FLOWERDEW, J.R. (1985) The ecological effects of the decline in rabbits *(Oryctolagus cuniculus L.)* due to myxomatosis. *Mammal Review,* **15,** 151-186

SWAN, M.S. (1991) *Rough Shooting.* Swan Hill, Shrewsbury.

SWIFT, J. (1986) Snipe. In: *The Atlas of Wintering Birds in Britain and Ireland.* Ed. P. Lack. British Trust for Ornithology, Tring.

TAPPER, S. (1976) The diet of weasels, *Mustela nivalis* and stoats, *Mustela erminea,* during early summer, in relation to predation on gamebirds. *Journal of Zoology, London,* **179,** 219-224.

TAPPER, S. (1979) The effect of fluctuating vole numbers *(Microtus agrestis)* on a population of weasels *(Mustela nivalis)* on farmland. *Journal of Animal Ecology,* **48,** 603-617.

TAPPER, S. (1982) The use of time-series analysis for game bag statistics. In: *Proceedings of the 2nd meeting of the Working Group on Game Statistics (International Union of Game Biologists).* Eds F. Leeuwenberg & I. Hepburn. Wildlife Management Division, Zoetermeer, Netherlands.

TAPPER, S. (1987) Cycles in game-bag records of hares and rabbits in Britain. *Symposium of the Zoological Society of London,* **58,** 79-98.

TAPPER, S. & PARSONS, N. (1984) The changing status of the Brown hare *(Lepus capensis L.)* in Britain. *Mammal Review,* **14,** 57-70.

TAPPER, S.C. & BARNES, R.F.W. (1986) Influence of farming practice on the ecology of the brown hare *(Lepus europaeus).* *Journal of Applied Ecology,* **23,** 39-52.

TAPPER, S.C., GREEN, R.E., & RANDS, M.R.W. (1982) Effects of mammalian predators on partridge populations. *Mammal Review,* **12,** 159-167.

TAPPER, S.C. & HIRONS, G. (1983) Recent trends in Woodcock Bags in Britain. *Proceedings of the 2nd European Woodcock and Snipe Workshop,* Ed. H. Kalchreuter. International Wildfowl Research Bureau, Slimbridge.

TAPPER, S.C., POTTS, G.R., & BROCKLESS, M. (1991) The Salisbury Plain predation experiment: the conclusion. *The Game Conservancy Review of 1990,* **22,** 87-91.

TAYLOR, W.L. (1946) The wild cat *(Felis sylvestris)* in Britain. *Journal of Animal Ecology,* **15,** 130-133.

TEGETMEIER, W.B. (1881) *Pheasants: their natural history and pratical management.* Horace Cox, London.

THOMPSON, H.V. (1964) Wild mink. *Agriculture,* **26,** 564-567.

THOMPSON, H.V. & WORDEN, A.N. (1956) *The Rabbit.* Collins, London.

TROUT, R.C., ROSS, J., & FOX, A.P. (1991) An experimental manipulation of Myxomatosis in a wild rabbit population *(Oryctolagus cuniculus)* in Britain. *Proceedings of the 18th Congress of the International Union of Game Biologists.* Eds B. Bobek, K. Perzanowski & W.L. Regelin. Krakow, Poland.

TROUT, R.C., TAPPER, S.C. & HARRADINE, J. (1986) Recent trends in rabbit populations in Britain. *Mammal Review,* **16**, 117-123.

TURNER, T.W. (1954) *Memoirs of a Gamekeeper.* Geoffrey Bles, London.

VANDERVELL, C.A. & COLES, C.L. (1980) *Game and the English Landscape.* Debrett's Peerage, London.

VAUGHAN, H.E.N., & VAUGHAN, J.A. (1968) Some aspects of the epizootiology of myxomatosis. *Symposium of the Zoological Society of London,* **24**, 289-309.

VENABLES L.S.V. & LESLIE P.H. (1942) The rat and mouse populations of corn ricks. *Journal of Animal Ecology,* **11**, 44-68.

WALTON, K.C. (1964) The distribution of the polecat *(Putorius putorius)* in England, Wales and Scotland, 1959-62. *Proceedings of the Zoological Society of London,* **143**, 333-336.

WALTON, K.C (1968) The distribution of the polecat, *Putorius putorius* in Great Britain, 1963-67. *Journal of Zoology, London,* **155**, 237-240.

WALTON, K.C. (1977) Polecat *Mustela putorius.* In: *The handbook of British Mammals.* Eds G.B. Corbet & H.N. Southern. Blackwells, Oxford.

WATSON, A & HEWSON, R. (1973) Population densities of mountain hares *Lepus timidus* on western Scottish and Irish moors and Scottish hills. *Journal of Zoology, London,* **170**, 151-159.

WATSON, A. & MILLAR, G.R, (1976) *Grouse Management.* Advisory Booklet **12**, The Game Conservancy, Fordingbridge.

WATSON, A. & MOSS, R. (1979) Population cycles in the Tetraonidae. *Ornis Fennica,* **56**, 87-109.

WATSON, D. (1977) *The Hen Harrier.* T. & A.D. Poyser, Berkhamsted.

WATSON, J.N.P. (1978) *Victorian and Edwardian Fieldsports from Old Photographs.* Batsford Ltd., London.

WILLES, G.A. (1961) National Wildfowl Counts 1948-61. In: *The New Wildfowler.* Eds N.M. Sedgewick, P. Whitaker & J. Harrison. Herbert Jenkins, London.

WILLIAMS, G.R. (1954) Population fluctuations in some northern hemisphere game birds (Tetraonidae). *Journal of Animal Ecology,* **23**, 1-37.

WILLIAMS, J. (1985) The statistical analysis of fluctuations in red grouse bag data. *Oecologia,* **65**, 269-272.

WILSON, J. (1983) Wintering site fidelity of Woodcock in Ireland. In: *Proceedings of the 2nd European Woodcock and Snipe Workshop.* Ed. H. Kalchreuter. International Wildfowl Research Bureau, Slimbridge.

WOODBURN, M.I.A., ROBERTSON, P.A. (1990) Woodland management for pheasants. In: *The Future of Wild Galliformes in the Netherlands.* Eds. J.T. Lumeij & Y.R. Hoogeveen. Organisatiecommissie Nederlandse Wilde Hoenders, Amersfoort, Netherlands.

YALDEN, D.W. (1976) The food of the hedgehog in England. *Acta Theriologica,* **21**, 30: 401-424.

YALDEN, D.W. (1984) The status of the Mountain hare, *Lepus timidus,* in the peak district. *Naturalist,* **109**, 55-59.

Acknowledgement of illustrations

Rodger McPhail drew the illustrations on pages, 18, 19, 34, 36, 38, 40, 42, 46, 56, 64, 66, 72, 88, 90, 92, 94, 96, 107 and 113 — all of which are from the Game Conservancy's collection. The illustrations on pages 10, 21, 22, 60, 62, 84, 109 and 112 are also by Rodger McPhail and are reproduced with permission from *"Come Dawn, Come Dusk"* © by Norman Mursell 1981, published by Unwin Hyman of Harper Collins Publishers Ltd. Likewise the drawings on pages 50 and 99 are by Rodger McPhail and come from *"Border Reflections"* by Lord Home and appear with his permission. The two other McPhail pictures on pages 26 and 82 come from *"Game and the English Landscape"* by Charles Coles and Anthony Vandervell with permission from Debrett's Peerage, the publishers. The drawings on pages 70, 74, 76, 78, and 80 are by Robert Gillmor and come from *"Predatory Mammals of Great Britain: a code of practice for their management"* edited by R.M. Stuttard and are reproduced with permission from the British Field Sports Society. Robert Gillmor also did the illustrations on pages 30 and 86 which are from the *"The Handbook of British Mammals; third edition"* edited by G.B. Corbet and S. Harris and are reproduced with permission from Blackwell Scientific Publications Ltd. The hare coursing sketch on page 28 is from a pencil drawing by Michael Lyne, with permission from Heale Gallery, Somerset TA10 OPQ. The gamekeeper on page 44 is by Will Garfit and is from The Game Conservancy collection, so is the woodcock on page 58 which is by Alex Jardine. The capercaillie on page 54 and the blackcock on page 52 are by Franz Mueller and appeared in the Proceedings of the Second International Grouse Symposium and are published with permission from the World Pheasant Association. The tufted ducks on page 68 are by Thelma Sykes and are reproduced with her permission and from the journal Wildfowl volume 41 in which they appeared. The picture of the sea otter on page 108 was drawn by Keith Bayha and is reproduced with his permission and from the US Fish and Wildlife Service in Anchorage. The Fenn trap picture on page 15 is reproduced with permission from Ian McCall's book *"Your Shoot"* published by A & C Black Ltd. The pheasant woodland cross section (pages 12 and 13) is from the late Nigel Gray's book *"Woodland Management for Pheasants"* published by David and Charles and reproduced with permission from Josephine Gray. The hare on page 32 is from François Bourlière's classic book *"The Natural History of Mammals"* and published by Alfred Knopf and Random House of Canada. The two maps on pages 4 and 5 are from *"Medieval England: an aerial survey"* by J.K.S. St Joseph and M.W. Beresford, published by Cambridge University Press and redrawn by Andrew Tapper. The map on page 55 was published by the Royal Society for Protection of Birds in their *"Conservation Review for 1988"*. The computer illustration on page 125 is taken from the Sirius Computer Handbook published by ACT of Birmingham.

The engravings on pages 14 and 48 are from Ralph Payne-Gallwey's *"Letters to Young Shooters"*, and those on pages 2, 3, 7, 8, 20 and 123 are from the *"Badminton Library: shooting"* by Lord Walsingham and Ralph Payne-Gallwey. The partridge drive on page 14 and the Holkham picture on page 13 come from *"The Country Life Library of Sport: shooting"* by Horace Hutchinson. The gin trap on page 15 is from *"Practical Game Preserving"* by W. Carnegie. The pheasant shooting picture in the Preface is from *"The Art of Shooting"* by Charles Lancaster; the highland shooter on page 9 is from *"In Grouseland"* by Evan Mackenzie and the muzzle loading gentlemen on page 6 is from an engraving by Thomas Bewick. The fur trading voyageurs on page 103 are from an engraving by C. Butterworth after an oil painting by Frances Ann Hopkins from the Public Archives of Canada, and the jolly gamekeeper who appears on pages 24 and 117 was the logo from the old ICI Researches In Game Biology series and appeared on the cover of Doug Middleton's 1934 paper on game population fluctuations.

INDEX